Teacher Annotated Edition

Human Sexuality

Mary Bronson Merki, Ph.D.

McGraw Hill **Glencoe**

New York, New York   Columbus, Ohio   Chicago, Illinois   Peoria, Illinois   Woodland Hills, California

Send all inquiries to:
Glencoe/McGraw-Hill
21600 Oxnard Street, Suite 500
Woodland Hills, California 91367

ISBN: 0-07-830945-X (Student Edition)
ISBN: 0-07-830946-8 (Teacher Annotated Edition)

3 4 5 6 7 8 9 073 09 08 07 06 05

Table of Contents

Introduction

Although statistics indicate that the number of teens who are sexually active is declining, we need to consider the following:

- The United States has the highest rates of teen pregnancy and births in the Western industrialized world.

- Approximately one in four new STD infections occur in teens, about 3.75 million cases each year. Teens and young adults are more likely than other age groups to have multiple sex partners and engage in unprotected sexual activity, putting them at high risk for acquiring most STDs.

- Because HIV can take up to ten years to progress to AIDS, most young adults between the ages of 20 and 29 were likely infected as teens. This is nearly one in every five reported AIDS cases.

Human Sexuality emphasizes using refusal skills, making responsible decisions, and practicing abstinence as ways to help reduce these statistics.

Using *Human Sexuality*

Most young people have received many messages about sex but know very little about sexuality. Some teens may have not had opportunities to discuss, in a serious manner, concerns and problems dealing with sexuality or to obtain factual information about it. Nor have they learned or had a chance to apply this practical information while practicing basic life skills, such as decision making, communication, goal setting, refusal, and the application of personal values in life. *Human Sexuality* presents factual information and encourages students to apply the information when making responsible decisions. There are several points about sexuality education you may wish to keep in mind to use the program successfully.

Parental Involvement

Education about sexuality is both a parent's or guardian's right and responsibility. Studies have shown that in homes where there is open communication on sexuality issues, young people tend to follow more traditional norms of sexual behavior. Efforts, thus, should be made to encourage parents or guardians to maintain an open and honest dialogue with their teens on sex-related issues raised in this program.

The most successful efforts in sexuality education are those that result from cooperation between home and school. Parents and guardians should be informed of sexuality programs, have an opportunity to review classroom materials, and, when possible, be provided with materials to use at home.

School and District Policies

Some schools may require parents to sign a letter of permission before their child takes the class. Are there school or state guidelines defining what can and cannot be taught in a class discussing sexuality issues? Find out exactly what the policies are for your school. It may be the case that student response to certain questions may require parental permission. Be aware of any such school and community guidelines before proceeding with this course.

The teacher is the critical key to whether a school-based sexuality program is successful. It is important that you feel comfortable with the subject matter and have a broad base of accurate information. Participating in update workshops as well as a sexuality course can be very helpful. Keep in mind the potential controversy that surrounds any program that includes sexuality topics. By being aware of the feelings and attitudes of the community and knowing how to handle sensitive topics, you may be able to avoid potential problems.

A Word About Refusal Skills

Human Sexuality reinforces the choice of sexual abstinence for young people and underscores the importance of avoiding all drugs, including alcohol. The choices to abstain from sexual activity before marriage and avoid risk behaviors including alcohol and drug use are viable options for teens. At the same time, and partly because of the role peer pressure and negative media messages play in teens' lives, discussions of and references to these subjects should be presented in a manner that is relevant and has immediacy for them. Telling students to just say no is not enough. Students must be provided with a knowledge base that can influence attitudes and help them choose healthy behaviors. *Human Sexuality* provides such a motivation, along with the opportunity for students to discuss concerns, learn to deal with and express feelings, and practice communication and assertiveness skills. *Human Sexuality* encourages students to use a decision-making process to make responsible choices and teaches valuable communication and refusal skills to help them stay out of situations that make them uneasy or that are unhealthy.

Program Components

Human Sexuality consists of a student text and a Teacher's Annotated Edition. Lesson plans are included to help you teach each lesson and chapter successfully and efficiently. Answers to Lesson and Chapter Reviews are provided in the Teacher Manual. Helpful Teaching Tips (indicated by the following headings: **DISCUSS**, **EMPHASIZE**, and **CRITICAL THINKING**) are found in the margins of each student page. These tips may be used to reinforce and enrich the material found in the lesson.

In addition to these teaching aids, you can receive help from guidelines under the headings *General Teaching Suggestions*, *Responding to Student Questions*, and *Use of Resources* which follow.

General Teaching Suggestions

The following are some tips for carrying out the lesson:

- Avoid using the word *you* in teaching (e.g., "When you participate in sexual activity . . .", which may be construed by students as an advocacy position. Instead, use the third-person pronoun in any class discussion.

- Acknowledge the fact that, historically, sexuality topics have not been discussed openly in our society. As such, some people are likely to be uncomfortable with them and may express this discomfort in any number of inappropriate ways (such as through laughter). Stress the inappropriateness of such responses, underscoring that sexuality is neither a forbidden topic nor one that should be confined to formal settings (i.e., the classroom).

- Correct the students' use of slang terms (to refer, for example, to parts of the reproductive system) by providing the students with correct terms. This simultaneously creates a trusting and mature environment and encourages free inquiry.

- Avoid asking for personal information or sharing such information about yourself with the class.

- If there are school or state guidelines defining what can and cannot be taught in a class discussing sexuality issues, explain the guidelines to the class. Then, if a question arises that goes beyond the district policy, the students can appreciate why it cannot be addressed in class. Students will support this approach and will not think that you are just dodging a topic.

- Emphasize, especially as you go through the material on teens and high-risk behaviors, that physical and emotional changes occurring during adolescence are normal and vary greatly from person to person. Most students' feelings, thoughts, and concerns are normal.

- Be sure to obtain permission (passive or active) from a parent or guardian prior to teaching about sexuality and/or STDs, as designated by state or local district guidelines. Note that student response to any questions may require prior parental or guardian permission.

- Emphasize mutual respect between students and between teacher and students regarding questions and answers and group participation.

- Encourage students to establish and maintain an open dialogue at home with their parents, guardians, or other adult care providers.

Responding to Student Questions

Here are some suggestions you may wish to follow when responding to student questions:

- All questions should be treated as serious questions. Do not assume that a student's question is being asked to elicit a reaction or get attention. If the question is one that goes beyond school guidelines, explain that fact to students. Advise students to pursue the line of inquiry with parents or in appropriate reference materials.

- Remind students that there is no such thing as a dumb question. Tell students you would rather they ask questions in class, where they can get correct information. Suggest that if they do ask a question, it is likely that others in class have the same question.

- Allow students to submit written questions anonymously if they do not feel comfortable speaking about a topic. Respond to written questions during class.

- Do not allow another student to answer a student's question, which risks not only throwing the discussion off track but disseminating incorrect information. If a student asks a question to which you do not know the answer, the appropriate response is to admit not having that information and to assure students that you will find the answer before the next class session. *Do not* give students the responsibility of hunting for every answer, as this may discourage future open inquiry.

- Repeat any difficult questions to be sure you heard them correctly.

- Answer all questions concisely, but bear in mind that most questions deserve more than a simple yes or no answer. Always take the time to review correct information and make sure students understand.

- Avoid making judgments or imposing your own opinions. This is often done in subtle ways through tone of voice or body language. Be aware of and spend extra time preparing for topics or issues on which you have particularly strong feelings that may be communicated to the class.

Remember, finally, that new information on topics related to sexuality is being made available on a continual basis, in both the newspaper and professional literature. It is important to stay abreast of current, accurate information from reliable sources and to be prepared to communicate this information to students in a format and style that will reach them.

Use of Resources

Here are some additional suggestions for the introduction and use of outside resource material:

- Any material brought into the classroom should be reviewed thoroughly. Some schools have guidelines concerning what can and cannot be used. Careless dissemination of material can have serious repercussions.

- All audiovisuals should be previewed before being shown. This point is critical. With such delicate subject matter, you will want to be thoroughly familiar with the contents of any video before presenting it.

- All potential guest speakers should be approved by the school administrator before being invited. You should discuss guidelines with the speaker prior to the presentation. In addition, the speaker should be advised of the main objectives of the course and the specific lesson.

Additional Resources

Information on topics related to sexuality is always changing, particularly in the area of sexually transmitted diseases and HIV/AIDS. The following page provides current information you may choose to use as a handout or part of your health class discussion. This page gives a synopsis of common STDs. This information corresponds with that in Chapter 7 of the student text. The chart includes a description of the STD, its cause, symptoms (when present), and treatment. It is important to remind students that in many cases, symptoms of STDs are not obvious.

SEXUALLY TRANSMITTED INFECTIONS

Disease	Description	Cause	Symptoms	Treatment
Chlamydia	An infection that attacks the male and female reproductive organs	The bacterium *Chlamydia trachomatis*	Females—(early) abnormal vaginal discharge, burning during urination; (late) PID, which involves severe pelvic pain, infertility, increased chance of ectopic pregnancy Males—(early) discharge from the penis, burning during urination; (late) damage to reproductive organs	Antibiotics
Gonorrhea	A disease that attacks the mucous membranes of the penis, vagina, uterus, rectum, throat	The bacterium *Neisseria gonorrhoeae*	Females—(early) yellow vaginal discharge, burning during urination; (late) PID Males—(early) yellow-whitish discharge from the penis, burning during urination, painful or swollen testicles; (late) epididymitis, infertility Both—(late) infection of blood or joints, which is life threatening	Antibiotics
Human Papillomavirus (HPV)	A virus that can cause genital warts, asymptomatic infection, and can cause cancer	Human papillomavirus (HPV)	Soft, moist, pink or red swellings—often in clusters on the genitals, anus, groin, or thigh; often asymptomatic	No cure; removal of warts by laser or by freezing, burning, cutting; injected antiviral drug; topical ointments
Genital Herpes	Blisters in the genital or rectal area	Herpes simplex virus type 2 (HSV-2)	Blisters within 2 weeks of contact, fever, swollen glands	No cure; antiviral drugs reduce duration and severity of episodes
Hepatitis B	A disease that attacks the liver	Hepatitis B virus (HBV)	Jaundice, fatigue, abdominal pain, nausea and vomiting, joint pain, loss of appetite	Drugs that are effective in about 40 percent of patients
Hepatitis C	A disease that causes liver damage	Hepatitis C virus (HCV)	Often asymptomatic; jaundice, fatigue, abdominal pain, loss of appetite, nausea and vomiting	Antiviral drugs, combination treatments effective in 40 to 80 percent of cases depending on type
Syphilis	A progressive disease that affects the entire body if left untreated	The bacterium *Treponema pallidum*	*Primary stage*—chancre, a painless sore *Secondary stage*—infectious rash on palms of hands and soles of feet; flulike symptoms, hair loss, weight loss *Late syphilis*—symptoms disappear during latent period, then slow, progressive loss of muscular coordination, paralysis, blindness, dementia, sometimes death	Antibiotics cure disease but cannot repair damage already done
Trichomoniasis and Bacterial Vaginosis	Vaginitis, or inflammation of the vagina; infection of the urethra in males (Trichomoniasis only)	The protozoan parasite *Trichomonas vaginalis* and an imbalance of bacteria normally found in the vagina, respectively	Females—odorous vaginal discharge; genital irritation, itching, discomfort Males—mild discharge from penis, irritation, burning (Trichomoniasis only)	Prescription drug metronidazole (for both)
Pubic Lice	Tiny parasitic insects that live in pubic hair and sometimes in coarse hair of legs, armpits, mustaches, beards, eyebrows, eyelashes	The parasitic insect *Phthirus pubis*	Intense itching in the genital area and/or other areas of infestation	Special medicated shampoo for pubic hair and hair of legs, armpits, mustaches, beards; special prescription ointment for eyebrows, eyelashes
Scabies	Microscopic mites that burrow into the skin	The parasitic mite *Sarcoptes scabiei*	Pimplelike rash with severe itching in the genital area and/or other areas of infestation 4–6 weeks after contact	Medicated lotions; additional medications for itching

Sexuality and Making Responsible Decisions

(pages 2–15)

 FOCUS

OBJECTIVES

- Explain how sexuality develops.
- Identify the physical, mental/emotional, and social changes that occur during adolescence.
- Identify decision-making skills that promote individual, family, and community health.
- Summarize the advantages of seeking advice and feedback when making healthful decisions.

MOTIVATOR

Write the following on the board for students to work on while attendance is being taken: *What kinds of product advertisements in magazine ads or television commercials promote products by using sexual messages?* Assign the Quick Start.

INTRODUCING THE LESSON

Allow students to describe the products that use sexual messages in their advertisements. Then discuss why so many advertisers use these types of messages to sell their products. (People want to identify with the people in the ad; sexual messages catch attention.)

INTRODUCING VOCABULARY

Have students look up the vocabulary words *self-concept* and *goal* in the Glossary/Glosario. Have them infer ways the two terms relate.

❷ TEACH

Discussing

Ask students whether they think popular entertainment—movies, television, and music—glamorizes sex. Discuss how they feel they are influenced by these sources. Then ask students to provide examples of songs, movies, or television shows that deal with the risks of sexual intercourse, such as unplanned pregnancy and sexually transmitted diseases. Have students discuss the frequency of these examples compared to the examples of sex being glamorized. **L1**

Discussing

Have students discuss the ways they have learned about sexuality. These could include a discussion with parents or information learned from a book. Record this list on the board. **L1**

Discussing

Point out that many of our decisions are influenced by peer pressure and that often this pressure is negative—that others try to convince us to do something unwise, unhealthy, or wrong. **L1**

Discussing

Put the following headings on the board: *Physical*, *Mental/Emotional*, and *Social*. Brainstorm and list ways to promote healthy sexuality in each area. **L1**

Cooperative Learning

Divide the class into four groups. Have each group work through the following problem using the decision-making model: One day while walking to school, one of three friends suggests skipping school and going to the local mall. Instruct the groups to begin by stating the situation that requires a decision and listing all of the possible options. Encourage them to be as thorough as they can. When discussing the group responses with the class, stress the role peer pressure might play in such a decision. **L2**

Class Activity

Ask each student to write down the names of three people he or she could talk to regarding an important decision about sexual activity. Tell students to keep this paper for future reference. **L1**

Cooperative Learning

Divide the class into four groups. Have each group choose a goal that a teen might set about dating. Then have students work through the goal-setting process. Evaluate the steps students have decided on and discuss the effects that both positive and negative peer pressure might have on such a goal. **L2**

Class Activity

Have students discuss the relationship between one's mental health and his or her self-concept. Ask students to create a list of people who influence a person's self-concept. Then discuss how positive role models can affect one's physical health. **L1**

Analyzing

Divide the class into females and males. Have each group compile a list of famous people (entertainers, politicians, businesspeople) that they consider to be typically "feminine" or "masculine." Have students list the characteristics that led to their choices. Use the lists to begin a discussion of how gender-role stereotypes get reinforced. **L1**

Class Activity

Have students reread the Health Minute on page 4. Ask students to suggest more examples of ways teens can meet their mental and emotional health needs. Ask what support systems are available to teens. Have volunteers discuss ways teens can reach out to the community and how this can contribute to good mental health. **L1**

3 ASSESS

EVALUATING THE LESSON

Assign and discuss the Lesson 1 Review on page 7.

Answers to Lesson 1 Review

1. Sexuality is everything about you as a male or female. Your sexuality develops over time as you live, grow, and develop.

2. The three aspects are physical health, mental/emotional health, and social health.
3. Self-concept is the mental image you have about yourself. It develops over time, beginning in infancy, from the variety of signals you get from people around you.
4. Break the decision-making process down into small steps, such as the six basic steps.
5. Answers will vary but should include aspects of physical growth and development and mental and emotional maturity, as well as basic physical and mental/emotional self-care discussed in the lesson.
6. Answers will vary but should demonstrate the student's understanding that a healthy self-concept promotes healthy, self-protective behavior, and a low self-concept makes self-destructive behavior more likely.

Answer to Applying Health Skills

Action plans will vary but should include the first four steps of the goal-setting process.

RETEACHING

Have students review the six goal-setting steps. Encourage them to explain in their own words how they would set about accomplishing a specific goal. Explain that the goal-setting steps can be used to reach both simple and complex goals.

ENRICHMENT

- Have students write a paragraph about how the influences on their social health change during adolescence.
- Have students write a paragraph about how using the decision-making process can help with important decisions.

4 CLOSE

Sum up the lesson by reminding students that adolescence is a time of tremendous change, and that they can make many important decisions that will promote their physical, mental/emotional, and social health.

Adolescence and Development

(pages 8–11)

OBJECTIVES

- Identify the developmental tasks of adolescence.
- Demonstrate strategies for communicating needs, wants, and emotions that lead to repsonsible behaviors.
- Analyze how changes during adolescence lead to an increased ability to have respect and empathy for other people.

MOTIVATOR

Write the following on the board for students to work on while attendance is being taken: *How does a child react to a difficult situation? How would you react to a difficult situation? Would an adult react differently?* Assign the Quick Start.

INTRODUCING THE LESSON

Have students share their answers from the Motivator and Quick Start activities. As a person moves from childhood to adolescence, his or her ability to handle difficult situations increases as he or she becomes more emotionally and intellectually mature. Tell students that in this lesson they will learn about tasks they need to accomplish before being ready to assume the responsibilities of adulthood.

INTRODUCING VOCABULARY

Tell students that the word *development* comes from the Old French word *desveloper,* which means "to unwrap" or "to expose." Have students look up the meaning of the suffix *-al* (relating to or characterized by) and use the meanings of the Old French word and the suffix to determine what the phrase *developmental tasks* might mean. Then have the students look up the term in the Glossary/Glosario and review the definition they find there.

② TEACH

Class Activity

Ask students to name skills they think an adult should have. List the responses on the board. Skills listed might include such things as filling out income tax forms or planning a family budget. After you have seven or eight skills listed, have students pick one skill and show how it relates to at least one of the developmental tasks. **L1**

Cooperative Learning

Divide the class into nine groups. Assign each group one of the developmental tasks listed in the lesson. Have each group develop a list of actions that would help an adolescent achieve that task. For example, one group may suggest that an adolescent could study vocabulary words for the SATs, which would expand his or her verbal skills. Groups should share their lists with the rest of the class. **L2**

Discussing

Ask students to explain how succeeding at each of the developmental tasks contributes to a person's ability to make responsible decisions. For example, developing behavioral maturity leads to behaving in a responsible manner, which is a result of making responsible decisions. **L1**

Using the Feature

Health Skills Activity

DECISION MAKING

After students have read the scenario, guide them through each step of the decision-making process on page 6. Have groups plan and present role-plays to demonstrate a health-enhancing decision Paul can make.

Research

Have students find articles and other sources of information about artificial intelligence. Ask them to write a short essay about the cognitive abilities of which computers are not yet capable. **L2**

③ ASSESS

EVALUATING THE LESSON

Assign and discuss the Lesson 2 Review on page 11.

Answers to Lesson 2 Review

1. A developmental task is something that needs to occur during a particular age period for a person to continue his or her growth toward maturity.
2. Answers will vary but should include four of the nine tasks outlined in the lesson.
3. The process of thinking and caring about other people is crucial to forming more mature relationships.
4. Answers will vary, but students should support their choices with clear reasoning.
5. Answers should reflect an understanding of the shift from concrete to abstract thinking, the ability to think logically, and the ability to appreciate finer points of an issue as well as others' views. Examples should demonstrate use of at least two of these higher-level thinking skills.

Answer to Applying Health Skills

Dialogues will vary, but one or more of the characters represented should be shown to behave responsibly, showing respect and empathy toward other characters.

RETEACHING

Have students review the list of developmental tasks from the lesson and explain in their own words what each task involves. Explain to them that just as toddlers need to learn certain tasks to progress to the next stage of childhood, they as adolescents need to accomplish these tasks to grow into capable, mature adults.

ENRICHMENT

To compare the reasoning abilities of people at different ages, have students develop a simple problem: *Your friends come by and want you to go to a movie with them. You haven't finished your chores/homework/work. What should you do? Why?*

Have students ask a 10-year-old, a 12-year-old, a 15-year-old, a 20-year-old, and a 30-year-old how each would solve the problem. Then have students compare the answers and discuss possible reasons for the differences they discover.

④ CLOSE

Sum up the lesson by reminding students that adolescence is a time of many changes. In fact, during adolescence, individuals experience the greatest degree of change in any period of life.

Lesson 3

Adolescence—A Time of Change

(pages 12–14)

① FOCUS

OBJECTIVES

- Identify and appraise the causes and significance of physical changes that occur during adolescence.
- Explain the role of hormones during puberty.
- Relate the development of secondary sex characteristics to chemical changes that occur within the body.

MOTIVATOR

Write the following on the board for students to work on while attendance is being taken: *What are some of the physical changes that take place during adolescence?* Assign the Quick Start.

INTRODUCING THE LESSON

Have students share their answers to the Motivator and Quick Start activities. Introduce the lesson by stating that during adolescence, individuals go through puberty. During puberty, hormones released by the pituitary gland and the gonads cause adolescents to grow and to develop secondary sex characteristics.

INTRODUCING VOCABULARY

Have students look up the words *hormones* and *pituitary gland* in the Glossary/Glosario. Then draw the following map on the board.

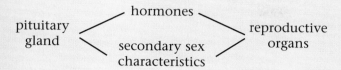

Beginning with "pituitary gland" and moving clockwise, help students explore the relationship illustrated: During adolescence, the pituitary gland releases hormones that stimulate the body to grow. Two of those hormones cause the reproductive organs to produce hormones of their own that cause the development of secondary sex characteristics. Have students suggest other words that might be added and branched out from the map.

② TEACH

Class Activity

Ask students to write down their height and gender on a piece of paper. Collect the papers and have students assist in creating a double bar graph or bar graphs for each gender. Have students compare the bars within each gender. Explain that the second fastest growth period of one's life occurs during puberty, when growth can be very uneven and varies greatly from person to person. At no other time in our lives is there such a difference in the sizes and shapes of people who are the same age.

Discussing

Have students interview one parent or guardian, using the following list of questions: What were the main concerns you had as a teen? What did your parents say about your choice of friends? In what kinds of social activities did you participate? Do not ask students to share the information they learned. Instead, conduct a class discussion about the overall interview experience. Ask students if the interviews made them feel any closer to their parents or guardians. Did they find out that the adult shared some of the same feelings they are now experiencing? Help students realize that their parents or guardians, like all adults, went through changes during puberty and experienced the concerns and problems of adolescence.

Class Activity

Have students create a chart with the following headings: *Male, Female,* and *Both Genders.* Then ask the students to complete the chart by filling in the secondary sex characteristics for each category. Lead a discussion about the similarities and differences between the genders.

Research

Have students find current articles on hormonal research related to growth or the reproductive system. Ask them to write a brief summary of the articles.

③ ASSESS

EVALUATING THE LESSON

Assign and discuss the Lesson 3 Review on page 14.

Answers to Lesson 3 Review

1. It is a body system made up of ductless glands that secrete chemicals called hormones into the blood.
2. Hormones released by the pituitary gland cause the changes that occur in the body during puberty. These hormones include growth hormones and hormones that affect the brain, glands, skin, bones, muscles, and reproductive organs.
3. The reproductive organs that produce sex cells are the testes in the male and the ovaries in the female.
4. Answers will vary but should reflect the student's understanding that developing secondary sex characteristics could affect a teen's self-image and prompt changes in relationships with peers and others.
5. Answers will vary but should include the widening physical differences between males and females. Students may focus on thinking differently about childhood friends of the opposite gender or may emphasize the need for more mature relationship skills.

Answers to Applying Health Skills

Posters will vary but should indicate an appreciation for the wide variations among adolescents in height, weight, and other developing physical characteristics. The tip for handling the stressor of concern about the differences should be practical.

RETEACHING

Have students write a short paragraph describing how the pituitary gland and hormones cause the changes that occur during puberty.

ENRICHMENT

Have students do further research on one gland or organ that is part of the endocrine system. Have them make a poster that includes a diagram of the gland or organ and lists its functions.

 CLOSE

Sum up the lesson by asking volunteers to describe two changes teens experience during puberty.

Chapter 1 Review Answers

Assign and discuss the Chapter 1 Review on page 15.

1. The facts will help you understand your growth and development and make decisions that protect your health and prevent some diseases.
2. Examples will vary, but students might suggest deciding not to participate in risky behavior that harms health.
3. Decision-making steps are 1.) State the situation. 2.) List the options. 3.) Weigh the possible outcomes. 4.) Consider values. 5.) Make a decision and act on it. 6.) Evaluate the decision.
4. Goal-setting steps are 1.) Select a goal and write it down. 2.) List the steps you will take to reach your goal. 3.) Identify sources of help and support. 4.) Set a reasonable time frame for reaching your goal. 5.) Evaluate your progress by establishing checkpoints. 6.) Reward yourself after achieving your goal.
5. Empathy is the ability to feel what others feel, to put yourself in someone else's place.
6. The pituitary gland does; it is located at the base of the brain.
7. The male organs are the testes; they release testosterone. The female organs are the ovaries; they release estrogen and progesterone.

8. Answers will vary but might include: males— shoulders broaden; facial, underarm, and pubic hair grows; voice deepens; muscles develop; bones become longer and larger; females— breasts develop; underarm and pubic hair grows; hips widen.
9. Answers will vary, but students could suggest decisions about behaviors such as using tobacco, drinking alcohol, taking illegal drugs, or becoming sexually active. Students should discuss how these decisions could affect all parts of their health.
10. Answers will vary.
11. Answers will vary.
12. Answers will vary but should focus on one of the higher-level thinking skills discussed in the chapter.
13. Answers will vary, but students should discuss that changes during adolescence occur at different rates.
14. The facial hair signals that this friend has begun to experience the changes of puberty. Answers should include informing the friend that hormones released during puberty cause the sweat glands in the body to become more active. As the sweat glands become more active, body odor can become a problem. The student may suggest to his friend that regular bathing is more necessary now than when they were younger.
15. Pamphlets will vary.
16. Stories will vary.

Encourage students to participate in activities that involve parents and community resources.

• Encourage students to complete this activity with a parent or other adult family member.
• Answers will vary.

Relationships and Communication (pages 16-21)

 FOCUS

OBJECTIVES

- Evaluate the effects of family relationships on physical, mental/emotional, and social health.
- Evaluate the positive and negative effects of relationships with peers.
- Demonstrate communication skills that build and maintain healthy relationships.

MOTIVATOR

Write the following on the board for students to work on while attendance is being taken: *Why do you think communication is important in any relationship?* Assign the Quick Start.

INTRODUCING THE LESSON

Have students share their responses to the Motivator and Quick Start activities. Tell students they will learn more about relationships and communication.

INTRODUCING VOCABULARY

Have students write their own definitions of the vocabulary terms and compare them with those in the Glossary/Glosario.

 TEACH

Discussing

Ask students to think about their relationships with immediate and extended family members. Point out that people are bonded to family members in many different ways—love, friendship, shared experiences and values. Ask students how the ways they develop friendships outside their families differ from ways they develop relationships within their families. How are they the same? **L1**

Class Activity

Let students work in small groups to role-play situations in which teens exert peer pressure. Encourage members to enact examples of both positive and negative pressure. **L1**

Discussing

Discuss with students the advantages of group dating. Brainstorm places in and around your town where people might go on a group date. **L1**

Cooperative Learning

Have each student bring in a picture from a magazine that is an example of nonverbal communication. Each student should write on the back of the picture what he or she thinks is being communicated. Tell students that there are no wrong answers for this activity. Allow each student to hold up his or her picture for the rest of the class to see. Call on two or three volunteers to say what they think is being communicated in the picture. Then, let the student read his or her remarks from the back of the photograph. Point out that different people can get different messages from nonverbal communication. The same is true for verbal, or spoken, communication. That is why it is important to practice the rules of good communication. **L2**

Demonstrating

After reading the section *Good Communication Skills*, have two student volunteers role-play the following activity. One person is *A*, the other is *B*. Explain that *A* promises to take *B* to a concert that starts at 7:30. *A* says he or she will pick up *B* at 6:45 but doesn't show up until 8:30. It's too late to go to the concert. *B* is furious. *B* is to confront *A* using "you" statements. After two or three minutes, stop the activity. Have two other student volunteers repeat the scene with *B* using only "I" messages. Remind the *Bs* to state how they feel and what they see as the problem. Allow two to three minutes. In a discussion, have students compare how *B* felt each time and how *A* felt each time. (Usually there is less finger-pointing and less defensiveness the second time.) **L1**

Analyzing

After students read the section *Good Listening Skills*, have each pick one skill he or she needs to work on. Ask each to make a plan describing what he or she will do to improve this skill. **L1**

Discussing

Have students describe examples of times that they worked out a compromise with someone. Ask them to explain how the compromise was to their advantage, and how they think it affected their relationship with the other person. **L1**

Discussing

Discuss how self-concept affects one's ability to have healthy relationships. **L1**

Analyzing

Ask students to think about why a couple might want to see each other exclusively. Ask students to list these reasons on a piece of paper and identify them as healthy or unhealthy reasons. Look at students' responses and share appropriate ones with the class for discussion. **L1**

Class Activity

Have students write a story that describes a successful group date. The story should tell what the group does, where it goes, and so on. Collect the papers, choose some that are suitable, and read them to the class. **L1**

Research

Have students find current articles that describe healthy relationships. Encourage them to include family relationships as well as friendships and dating relationships. **L2**

ASSESS

EVALUATING THE LESSON

Assign and discuss the Lesson 1 Review on page 21.

Answers to Lesson 1 Review

1. Parents, guardians, and other family members help you learn to get along with other people. Your family teaches you your basic values and helps you learn to function in society.
2. Peer pressure is the influence that people your own age may have on you. A teen with low self-esteem is more likely to conform to peer pressure even if it means engaging in high-risk behaviors or other activities that go against his or her values.
3. Benefits include: You have opportunities to interact with a variety of people, you can get to know individuals better at the same time, and you may feel less nervous on a first date.
4. If you use good communication skills, you will find it easier to talk calmly about a problem. For example, if you use "I" messages, you are less likely to provoke a conflict by making the other person feel blamed. Keeping a respectful tone and being clear and organized about the problem would also help you stay calm.
5. Answers will vary but might include participating in a variety of social activities. Becoming a good friend might involve helping your friend with a task or a project and using good communication and listening skills.

Answers to Applying Health Skills

Lists will vary.

RETEACHING

Have students reread the five suggestions for good communication on page 19. Have them explain in their own words how they would approach a particular conflict with a friend. Explain that good communication skills can be used to resolve conflicts with people they are close to and others whom they don't know as well.

ENRICHMENT

Divide the class into males and females. Have each group make a list of the five qualities they look for in a friend. Have the class compare lists. Then have them discuss the following question: How do the qualities change when considering someone to date?

4 CLOSE

Summarize this lesson by telling students that the material in this lesson presented skills to help them communicate well and build healthy relationships. In the next lesson they will learn about making decisions about sexual relationships.

Lesson 2

Decisions About Sexual Relationships (pages 22–26)

1 FOCUS

OBJECTIVES

- Analyze the importance and benefits of abstinence from sexual activity before marriage in promoting emotional health and preventing pregnancy, STDs, and HIV/AIDS.
- Evaluate ways to practice abstinence in a dating relationship.
- Demonstrate refusal skills to reinforce the decision to remain abstinent.

MOTIVATOR

Write the following on the board for students to work on while attendance is being taken: *List three reasons for teens to practice abstinence from sexual activity.* Assign the Quick Start.

INTRODUCING THE LESSON

Have students share their reasons for practicing abstinence. Explain that in this lesson students will study reasons to wait until marriage to engage in sexual activity.

INTRODUCING VOCABULARY

Have students write their own definitions of what they believe intimacy and refusal skills might be. Have them look up the words in the Glossary/Glosario and compare the actual definition to their own. Emphasize that intimacy involves physical and emotional closeness. Tell students they will learn more about intimacy and its relationship to abstinence.

2 TEACH

Research

Have students conduct research to find out if there are local or national organizations formed to encourage abstinence. Ask students to design their own organization and describe ways it would help members in their commitment to remain abstinent. **L1**

Demonstrating

After reading the section on refusal skills, allow students to meet in groups to role-play teens using refusal skills to say "no" to high-risk behaviors, such as drinking alcohol. **L1**

Analyzing

Reread *Did You Know* on page 26. Ask students to think about a friendship or dating relationship of their own and whether or not this relationship supports their rights. **L1**

Using the Feature

Health Skills Activity

REFUSAL SKILLS

Remind students to include specific strategies for effective refusals in their dialogues. Allow time for volunteers to present their dialogues to the class and discuss the effective use of communication and refusal skills.

3 ASSESS

EVALUATING THE LESSON

Assign and discuss the Lesson 2 Review on page 26.

Answers to Lesson 2 Review

1. Abstinence is a deliberate decision to avoid harmful behaviors, including sexual activity before marriage and the use of alcohol, tobacco, and other drugs.
2. Any four of the following: Abstinence can allow a couple to build a deeper friendship; abstinence eliminates both persons' risks of contracting a sexually transmitted disease; abstinence is the only 100 percent effective

method to avoid unplanned pregnancy; engaging in sexual activity is against one's values; being sexually active can interfere with a person's future plans; one may not feel physically, mentally, emotionally, or financially ready for sexual activity or its consequences.

3. Any three of the following: Use decision-making skills; say no, repeat yourself if necessary; be polite but firm; suggest alternative activities; do not compromise; avoid the use of alcohol and other drugs; leave if necessary. Examples will vary.

4. Answers will vary. Students may suggest to their friend that it is easier to decide about limits on sexual behavior before he or she is in a situation where sexual feelings build up. A well thought-out plan of action will help him or her to abstain from sexual activity.

5. Answers will vary. Possible physical consequences include sexually transmitted diseases and unplanned pregnancy. Possible mental/emotional consequences include feelings of guilt, broken trust with parents and friends, and anxiety about possible pregnancy or disease. Legal consequences exist for any adult who has sexual contact with anyone under the age of consent, which varies from state to state.

Answer to Applying Health Skills

Answers will vary. Plays should feature appropriate dating situations. The characters should emphasize the idea of planning the details of the date and avoiding situations where alcohol or other drugs may be present.

RETEACHING

Have students use their own words to describe refusal skills.

ENRICHMENT

Have students write a letter to a younger family member or neighbor in which they coach the younger person on a specific situation requiring the use of refusal skills. Students should also remind the younger person of their rights in a relationship.

4 CLOSE

Sum up the lesson by asking students to list the three most important things they learned in this lesson.

Chapter 2 Review Answers

Assign and discuss the Chapter 2 Review on page 27.

1. family
2. Communication is the process through which you send messages to and receive messages from others.
3. By using an "I" message, you are taking responsibility for your feelings. A "you" statement seems to blame someone else and can cause the listener to become defensive and unwilling to talk about the problem.
4. Any four of the following: Give your full attention to the person speaking and eliminate distractions; focus on the speaker's message by looking for the central concept; indicate your interest; remember what the speaker has said; use positive body language.
5. Issues to consider include: pressure from a boyfriend or girlfriend to engage in sexual activity; differing from a boyfriend or girlfriend regarding feelings about premarital sexual activity; the benefits of abstinence; communication about expectations of the relationship with a boyfriend or girlfriend; and the effects of engaging in sexual activity on the teen and his or her family.
6. Intimacy is closeness between two people that develops over time. A couple can hold hands, hug, kiss, and grow to know and understand each other to establish intimacy while practicing abstinence.
7. You can plan the location of the date, the amount of time that you will spend on the date, and when you will go home. Answers will vary, but may discuss how planning safe activities can help teens avoid risky situations.
8. Refusal skills are communication strategies that help you say no effectively.
9. Charts will vary. Students may list values such as honesty, trust, and respect.
10. Peer pressure can have a positive effect if friends also practice abstinence themselves. Peer pressure can have a negative effect if sexually active friends make a person feel that he or she needs to change behavior to belong to the group.

11. Answers will vary. Students may suggest that if the dating partner does not respect the person's decision, he or she may not be right for the person.

12. Answers will vary. Students may point out that teens who practice abstinence are mature because they have considered the consequences of sexual activity and decided to avoid taking the associated risks. Teens who practice abstinence may be considered independent because they are not giving in to the direct and indirect pressure from peers, friends, media, and other sources to engage in sexual activity.

13. Answers will vary. Student responses should incorporate the principles of dating someone who shares interests and values; using good communication skills; learning how to resolve conflict without compromising values; and deciding in advance their personal limits on sexual behavior.

14. Answers will vary. Student responses should incorporate the ideas of setting guidelines in advance, avoiding high-risk situations, and using refusal skills.

15. Skits will vary.

16. Stories will vary.

17. Pamphlets will vary.

BEYOND *the* Classroom

Encourage students to participate in activities that involve parents and community resources. Answers will vary.

Lesson 1

The Male Reproductive System

(pages 28–34)

 FOCUS

OBJECTIVES

- Analyze the relationship between good personal hygiene, health promotion and disesase prevention
- Describe the functioning of the male reproductive system.
- Relate the importance of early detection and warning signs that prompt individuals to seek health care for the male reproductive system.

MOTIVATOR

Write the following on the board for students to work on while attendance is being taken: *How can you take care of your reproductive system?* Assign the Quick Start.

INTRODUCING THE LESSON

Have students share their answers to the Motivator and Quick Start activities. Tell students that their reproductive systems are inactive until puberty. Then the reproductive systems of both males and females change and begin to function. This is why it is especially important at this time for adolescents to learn how the reproductive systems work and how to care for them. Students may discuss personal hygiene and monthly self-examinations.

INTRODUCING VOCABULARY

Have students look over the list of vocabulary words and note any similarities between the words they can find. Some of these similarities may be obvious, such as *testes* and *testosterone*. Tell students that the word *epididymis* comes from the Greek

word *didymos*, meaning "testicle." Have them find other words in the list that relate to one another.

2 TEACH

Class Activity

Review the parts of the male reproductive system. Have students examine the path of the sperm on the illustration of the male reproductive system. Tell them that sperm are produced in the testes and then move to the epididymis at the back of the testes, where they mature. The sperm then travel into the vas deferens, which becomes the ejaculatory duct as it passes through the prostate gland. Secretions from the seminal vesicles empty into the ejaculatory duct and join with the sperm and secretions from the testes. Secretions from the prostate gland and the Cowper's glands are the final components that make up semen. The ejaculatory duct opens into the urethra, through which the semen exits the body. **L1**

Discussing

Discuss with students the risks of STDs to the male reproductive system. Have students work in groups and investigate descriptions, symptoms, and treatment of one STD. You may wish to refer to the table on STDs on page TM8. **L1**

Research

Have students find current articles about testicular and prostate cancer and their treatment. Review the articles and then allow students to share them with the class. **L2**

3 ASSESS

EVALUATING THE LESSON

Assign and discuss the Lesson 1 Review on page 34.

Answers to Lesson 1 Review

1. The scrotum is a loose sac of skin that hangs outside the body. It holds the testes. The testes

are the male sex glands, and they manufacture testosterone and produce sperm. To produce sperm, the temperature of the testes must be a few degrees lower than normal body temperature. The scrotum keeps the testes at the right temperature by holding the testes away from or close to the body as needed.

2. The external organs are the scrotum, testes, and penis. The internal organs are the vas deferens, the seminal vesicles, the prostate gland, Cowper's glands, and the urethra.

3. Care of the male reproductive system includes thorough washing of the external organs and monthly testicular self-examination.

4. Possible answer: Cancer of the testes can be detected through monthly testicular self-examination.

5. Sperm are produced in a section of the testes called the seminiferous tubules. Next they move into the epididymis, where they mature. From the epididymis, sperm travel into the vas deferens. The vas deferens loops over the pubic bone, around the bladder, and through the prostate gland. As it passes through the prostate gland, it narrows and becomes the ejaculatory duct, which opens into the urethra. The urethra carries semen out of the body through the tip of the penis.

6. Possible answers: If the seminal vesicles did not function properly, the sperm would not receive nourishment and be mobile. If the prostate gland did not function properly, acids in the urethra and those encountered during intercourse in the vagina would destroy the sperm. If the Cowper's glands did not function properly, the acidity of any urine that might be in the urethra would destroy the sperm.

Answer to Applying Health Skills

Answers will vary, but students might research chlamydia, gonorrhea, or human papillomavirus.

RETEACHING

Using the diagram on page 32, point out each internal and external organ in the male reproductive system. Ask students to describe the function of each organ.

ENRICHMENT

Have students research the causes of fertility problems in men. Have them find articles about typical treatments for each of these problems and report their findings to the class.

④ CLOSE

Sum up the lesson by asking students why it is important for males to practice good personal hygiene and care for the health of the male reproductive system. In the next lesson they will learn about the female reproductive system.

Lesson 2

The Female Reproductive System
(pages 35–43)

① FOCUS

OBJECTIVES
- Describe the functioning of the female reproductive system.
- Relate the importance of early detection and warning signs that prompt individuals to seek health care for the female reproductive system.
- Analyze the relationship between good personal hygiene and disease prevention.

MOTIVATOR
Write the following on the board for students to work on while attendance is being taken: *How is the female reproductive system different from the male reproductive system?* Assign the Quick Start.

INTRODUCING THE LESSON
Have students share their answers from the Motivator and Quick Start activities. Tell students that in this lesson, they will learn about the parts of the female reproductive system and the function of each part.

INTRODUCING VOCABULARY
Have students look at the vocabulary words for this lesson. Then ask students which word comes from the Latin word *mensis*, meaning "month" *(menstruation)*.

② TEACH

Class Activity

Refer students to the illustration of the female reproductive system. Pronounce the name of each organ in the system. Review the function of each organ. Points to emphasize include: (1) Unlike in a male, there are two openings in the female genital area. One opening is the urethra, which leads to the bladder. Urine is stored in the bladder and leaves the body through the urethra. This is part of the excretory system and has nothing to do with the reproductive system in females. (2) The other opening is the vagina, which is part of the reproductive system. A common misconception is that if a female urinates after intercourse, she will rinse out sperm and not get pregnant. Ask students why this is incorrect. (Urine leaves the body through the urethra; sperm enters through the vagina.) L1

Discussing

Point out that it is important during puberty to learn to care for your reproductive system. For females, this includes practicing good personal hygiene and performing monthly breast self-examinations. It also means having annual pelvic examinations by a health care professional after the age of 18 or earlier if one is sexually active. L1

Discussing

Tell students that one out of every eight females living in the United States has a risk of developing breast cancer during her lifetime. Remind students that while breast cancer is the most common form of cancer in American females, it also occurs in males, though it is relatively rare (about 1 percent of all breast cancer cases). Ask students why it is important that males learn about breast cancer. L1

Guest Speaker

Invite a representative from the American Cancer Society to present information to the class on cervical cancer. Be sure to explain to the speaker any school guidelines regarding how much detail and what kind of information should be shared and ask to preview any audiovisual resources that will be used. L1

Using the Feature

Real-Life Application

ACCESSING INFORMATION

Encourage students to examine the Web page provided on page 41 to verify the elements of a valid source of information. Have them check the site's sponsor, verify additional links, and identify citations from specific sources. Ask students to summarize the reliability of this resource in a paragraph.

Discussing

Ask students why it is important to answer all of a physician's medical questions as truthfully as possible. Explain that the more a physician knows about a patient's medical history, the better prepared the physician is to diagnose any problems a patient might have. Encourage students to ask questions during checkups, especially during pelvic exams. The more a person asks, the better he or she understands the process. L1

③ ASSESS

EVALUATING THE LESSON

Assign and discuss the Lesson 2 Review on page 43.

Answers to Lesson 2 Review

1. The cervix is the neck of the uterus. The uterus is a hollow, muscular organ that receives and holds the fertilized ovum during pregnancy. The primary function of the uterus is to hold and nourish a developing embryo and fetus. The cervix has a very small opening that dilates, or opens up, to allow a baby to pass out of the uterus during birth.
2. The external organs are the mons pubis, labia majora, labia minora, vaginal opening, and clitoris. The internal organs are the vagina, uterus, fallopian tubes, and ovaries.
3. Breast cancer can be detected through monthly self-examination and also through annual mammograms, which are recommended for all women after age 40. Cervical cancer can be detected by getting an annual Pap test.
4. Care of the female reproductive system includes good personal hygiene, monthly breast self-exams, and regular examinations by

a physician, including a Pap test after age 18 or earlier if sexually active.

5. Answers will vary, but students should include strategies listed on page 39.

6. Paragraphs will vary but should mention finding out if there is an odorless or odorous discharge and testing in some way to identify the responsible organism.

Answer to Applying Health Skills

Letters will vary, but students should note that a Pap test can detect cervical cancer in the early stages, which is easier to treat than in later stages, and that risk factors for cervical cancer include being between the ages of 20 and 30 and not having regular Pap tests. Letters should present the student's case convincingly.

RETEACHING

Using the diagram on page 37, point out each internal and external organ in the female reproductive system. Ask students to name and describe the function of each organ.

ENRICHMENT

Have students research various methods of alleviating the pain of abdominal cramps early in the menstrual period. Ask students which methods they think will work best and why.

Sum up the lesson by asking students the three most important things they learned in this lesson. Emphasize how important it is for females to keep themselves and their reproductive systems healthy.

Lesson 3

Hormones and Sexual Feelings

(pages 44–46)

OBJECTIVES
- Examine the effect of hormones on body systems.

- Demonstrate healthful decision-making skills that show responsible behavior for your health and the health of others.

MOTIVATOR

Write the following on the board for students to work on while attendance is being taken: *Why is it important to set personal limits on sexual behavior before getting involved in a situation where sexual feelings are present?* Assign the Quick Start.

INTRODUCING THE LESSON

Have students share their answers to the Motivator and Quick Start activities. Explain that when in an emotional state such as sexual excitement, it may be easy to be overwhelmed by such feelings and more difficult to make a responsible decision. Students should recognize that having predetermined limits will help them stick to their responsible choices during stressful times.

INTRODUCING VOCABULARY

Write the term *hormones* on the board. Have volunteers recall the definition from Chapter 1. Then have students look up the word in the Glossary/Glosario.

❷ TEACH

Discussing

Ask students to discuss the difference between love and sexual excitement. Emphasize that love is an emotional feeling, while sexual excitement is an automatic physiological response. Explain that some people may confuse the two, but that it is important to remember that sexual excitement is a result of hormones being released. **L1**

Class Activity

Have students consider the relationship between how a person chooses to respond to sexual feelings and the effects of that response on a person's long-term goals. Ask volunteers to give examples of how responsible decisions regarding sexual activity can be made by keeping goals in mind. **L1**

Using the Feature

Discussing

Have students discuss the following statement: *A couple can have a long-lasting relationship that does not include sexual intercourse.* **L1**

3 ASSESS

EVALUATING THE LESSON

Assign and discuss the Lesson 3 Review on page 46.

Answers to Lesson 3 Review

1. Sex hormones cause the body to respond to sexual stimulation.
2. Answers may include any four of the following: the heart rate increases, breathing speeds up, hands feel clammy, the face gets flushed, the penis swells, the vaginal walls swell, the vagina becomes lubricated, the clitoris swells.
3. Once sexual tension builds up, it is more difficult to make a responsible decision. It is smarter and easier to have predetermined limits on sexual behavior and stop things before they progress.
4. Sexual feelings are not the same as love. Sexual feelings are triggered by hormones and involve a physical response to a stimulating situation or thought. Love is a deep *emotional* bond, not an automatic response.
5. Answers will vary, but students may note that thinking about something they really want in the future can motivate them to plan ahead and to preset limits on sexual behavior to protect those goals or remind them of what they could lose if they do not act responsibly.

Answer to Applying Health Skills

Cartoons will vary but should demonstrate an understanding that the goal provides a positive influence on decisions about how to spend time with a date without testing their resistance to building sexual tension.

RETEACHING

Explain that we cannot keep our hormones from causing sexual feelings. Emphasize, however, that while we have no control over the hormones, we have control over how we react to those feelings and are able to make responsible decisions about them.

ENRICHMENT

Have students research the hormones affecting the autonomic nervous system, the system that helps maintain the body's metabolism. Have them present a report or prepare a video to share this information with the rest of the class.

4 CLOSE

Sum up the lesson by telling students that this lesson is intended to support young people in making responsible decisions about sexual activity.

Chapter 3 Review Answers

Assign and discuss the Chapter 3 Review on page 47.

1. The epididymis is a highly coiled structure located on the back side of each testis. Over a period of 64 days, sperm produced in each testis mature in the epididymis.
2. The urethra.
3. Semen is made up of sperm and secretions from the testes, secretions from the seminal vesicles that nourish sperm and help make them mobile, secretions from the prostate that neutralize acids in the urethra and the vagina, and secretions from the Cowper's glands that lubricate the urethra and neutralize acidity of any urine that is present.
4. Activities such as heavy lifting can result in inguinal hernia.
5. The fallopian tubes are tubes on each side of the uterus that connect the uterus to the region of the ovaries. When an ovum is released from an ovary, motions of the fingerlike projections at the end of the tube near the ovary draw the ovum into the tube. Fertilization usually occurs in the widest part of the tube.

6. Menstruation usually begins between the ages of 10 and 15.

7. For males, any three: overheating of the testes, exposure to certain chemicals, contracting mumps as an adult, an untreated STD, and problems with the epididymis, vas deferens, or urethra. For females, any three: physical blocking of one or both fallopian tubes, failure to ovulate (usually for hormonal reasons), endometriosis, and untreated STDs.

8. Symptoms include a change in breast or nipple appearance, a lump or swelling in the breast, and a lump in the armpit.

9. Answers will vary, but students should discuss the importance of cleanliness, care in lifting heavy objects, self-exams for males and females, regular physical exams, and seeing a health care professional when a possible problem occurs.

10. Forty-six chromosomes are needed—23 from the male's sperm and 23 from the female's ovum.

11. It is the only body system that is different for males and females.

12. Ovulation must occur before fertilization can take place. Menstruation does not occur if fertilization has taken place.

13. Dialogues will vary, but students should point out that vaginal infections are fairly common and could have many causes, some of which require prescribed medication.

14. Answers will vary, but students should demonstrate a caring attitude and should explain that changes during the teen years are normal and what this means in terms of their sibling's maturing body.

BEYOND *the* Classroom

- Encourage parents to meet with the school nurse during or before the classroom visit. Issues to discuss may include dating, peer pressure, abstinence, sexually transmitted diseases (including HIV infection), and pressure to use drugs and alcohol.

- Answers will vary but should indicate that students recognize the range and depth of training and personal qualifications needed for the profession.

Lesson 1

The Commitment to Marry

(pages 49–54)

1 FOCUS

OBJECTIVES

- Analyze behavior in a dating relationship that will enhance the dignity, respect, and responsibility relating to marriage.
- Distinguish between a dating relationship and a marriage.
- Demonstrate how couples use effective communication skills in building and maintaining healthy relationships.
- Describe the effects of divorce on adults and children.
- Explain why teens should delay marriage until they are mature adults.

MOTIVATOR

Write the following on the board for students to work on while attendance is being taken: *Do you plan to marry? If so, at what age do you think you will marry?* Assign the Quick Start.

INTRODUCING THE LESSON

Have students share their answers to the Motivator and Quick Start. Write the number of students who plan to marry on the board. Then write the ages at which these people indicated they think they will marry. Have students calculate the average ages for each gender. Compare the figures for your class with the following statistic:

The average age for first marriages in the United States is about 27 for males and 25 for females.

INTRODUCING VOCABULARY

Tell students that the word *commitment* comes from the Latin word *committere*, which means "to connect" or "to entrust." Ask students how these word origins relate to the commitment of marriage. (In a marriage, you share a special connection with another person, whom you have entrusted to share your life with you.)

2 TEACH

Discussing

Ask students to create a list of reasons why two adults might marry. Have students explain why it is important for a person to be mentally and emotionally mature before entering into a marriage.

Using the Feature

Health Skills Activity

COMMUNICATION

Have students work in groups to brainstorm ideas for resolving the conflict between Tom and Alicia. Remind them to include interaction and use of effective communication skills in their endings to the scenario. Allow time for groups to present their role-plays to the class.

Class Activity

Have students compile a list of television shows that depict divorced or blended families. Have them discuss some of the problems experienced by the parents and children in those families.

Discussing

Have students discuss the reasons why most teen marriages do not last. Then discuss problems that occur in teen marriages. (Responses may include a desire to go to college, wanting the freedom to go out with their friends when they want to, and not wanting to be tied down.)

③ ASSESS

EVALUATING THE LESSON

Assign and discuss the Lesson 1 Review on page 54.

Answers to Lesson 1 Review

1. A commitment is a promise or a pledge. Answers will vary, but should include lifelong commitment and readiness to take on responsibilities of marriage.
2. The couple faces these challenges and demonstrates communication and compassion.
3. A blended family is a family where two adults marry and have children from a previous marriage living with them.
4. Marrying young can interfere with a teen's personal growth and development; marrying young may force a teen to postpone college, job training, or beginning a career; marrying young because of pregnancy places emotional and financial stresses on the relationship.
5. Answers will vary, but students should discuss how maturity, commitment, and mutual love and respect contribute to the dignity, respect, and responsibilities of a healthy marriage.
6. Answers will vary, but possible negative effects of divorce may include: one parent moving out, facing potential financial difficulties, and dealing with difficult emotions. Healthful ways for family members to deal with divorce include keeping the lines of communication open; talking to relatives and other trusted adults; and seeking help and support from a professional counselor or a support group.

Answer to Applying Health Skills

Answers will vary. Students should thoroughly analyze the media marriage they selected and provide specific reasons to back up their opinions.

RETEACHING

Have students review the list of reasons why teens should delay marriage. Remind students that marriage takes a great deal of work and patience.

ENRICHMENT

Have students collect the age data on divorce rates for different states. Ask whether their findings

support the correlation between early marriage and divorce.

④ CLOSE

Sum up the lesson by telling students that successful marriages occur when two people are mentally and emotionally mature and are willing to work through their problems together. In the next lesson students will learn about some of the responsibilities of a good parent.

Lesson 2

Becoming a Parent (pages 55–60)

① FOCUS

OBJECTIVES

- Identify reasons why people have children.
- Describe the roles and responsibilities of parents in promoting healthy families.
- Evaluate the effects of family relationships on physical, mental/emotional, and social health.
- Analyze the importance and benefits of abstinence.

MOTIVATOR

Write the following on the board for students to work on while attendance is being taken: *Do you want to have children in the future? What are some reasons to have children?* Assign the Quick Start.

INTRODUCING THE LESSON

On the board, write the number of students who indicated in the Motivator that they would like to have children in the future. With the class, calculate this percentage for both genders. Then have students share their reasons for wanting to be parents. Write this list on the board and have students compare this list to the reasons listed in the lesson.

INTRODUCING VOCABULARY

Write the following vocabulary term on the board: *parenting*. Have students write their idea of what this word means and then check the definition in the dictionary and Glossary/Glosario.

②TEACH

Class Activity

Have students create a list of reasons why it is important to be both physically and emotionally mature before making the decision to become a parent. Remind students to think of both the child and the parents when creating their lists. **L1**

Guest Speaker

Invite a parenting instructor to speak to your class about the responsibilities and tasks involved in raising children. **L1**

Class Activity

Have students refer to nutrition charts to compare the dietary needs of a pregnant and nonpregnant female. Have students plan a three-day meal plan for a pregnant female. **L1**

Discussing

Ask students to discuss the social consequences of teen parenthood. What would be the impact on a teen's family if he or she became a parent? **L1**

Research

Have students research the median salaries of people with different levels of education. Ask them to compare the average salary of a person who has not completed high school to one who has a college degree. Have students use these figures to explain why teen parents are less likely to be able to provide financially for a child. **L2**

③ASSESS

EVALUATING THE LESSON

Assign and discuss the Lesson 2 Review on page 60.

Answers to Lesson 2 Review

1. Reasons include: they love children; they want to pass on the family name and heredity; they wish to give one's parents a grandchild; they want to be loved by someone; they are giving in to pressure from friends or parents; and they hope to bring stability to a shaky marriage.

2. Teens are less likely to get proper medical attention, may not have a well-balanced diet, and have a higher risk of medical complications such as early or prolonged labor, high blood pressure, and anemia; these factors may compromise the health of the mother and the baby.

3. A teen father may need to quit high school to get a job to help support the child; the lack of a diploma might make it difficult to find a high-paying job; there could be emotional and social health problems.

4. Teen parents often depend on their families for financial and emotional support. Meeting the needs of mother and infant puts a strain on families. Dropping out of school and juggling schedules impacts social health.

5. Answers will vary, but students should mention examples of the parents' responsibility to meet the child's physical, mental, emotional, and social needs.

6. Answers will vary. Students may suggest problems with parents, peers, and the other parent of the child; problems with school, and health problems associated with the pregnancy.

Answer to Applying Health Skills

Answers will vary. Refusal statements may convey the risk of complications during pregnancy, not being able to finish high school, not having an adequate income, having to give up a normal social life, giving up goals such as attending college, having to care for a baby 24 hours a day.

RETEACHING

Have students write a short paragraph describing the qualities necessary to be a nurturing and committed parent.

ENRICHMENT

Have students observe a day-care center or assist a family with small children for several hours. Ask students to write an essay about the difficulties involved in caring for children.

④CLOSE

Sum up the lesson by telling students that becoming a parent is a great responsibility that requires both physical and emotional maturity. Remind students that teen parents will experience many difficulties.

Chapter 4 Review Answers

Assign and discuss the Chapter 4 Review on page 61.

1. To enter a lasting relationship with the person they love
2. They understand their needs and know how to meet them in healthy ways.
3. Students' answers should include any four of the factors in the bulleted list under the head "Adjusting to Marriage."
4. Approximately 50 percent
5. Parenting is providing care, support, and love in a way that leads to a child's total development. The most basic function is taking care of physical needs, such as food, clothing, shelter, and medical care.
6. She has a greater risk for complications in pregnancy, including miscarriage, and her body is not fully developed and is often not prepared for the stresses of pregnancy.
7. Students may list dropping out of school, not being able to get a good job, finding ways to spend time with his child, and being financially responsible for a child.
8. Practicing abstinence from sexual activity before marriage.
9. Answers will vary, but may include level of maturity, their ability to make healthy decisions, relationship with family members, educational and career goals, and personal choices about whether one would like to be a parent someday.
10. Answers will vary, but students might discuss differences of opinion about important issues concerning their relationship, such as different interests, different backgrounds, different religions; arguments about finances; and disagreements about whether to have children and how to raise them.
11. Answers will vary. Students should point out attributes of the healthy marriage and attributes of the unhealthy marriage.
12. Answers will vary.
13. Answers will vary, but students might suggest that some people are better parents because they are mature, have prepared for parenthood, and have experienced positive family influences in the past.
14. Answers will vary. Student responses should provide specific examples for comparing and contrasting and discuss the difficulties of raising a baby as a single teen.
15. Pamphlets will vary.
16. Stories will vary.

BEYOND the Classroom

Encourage students to participate in activities that involve parents and the community. Answers will vary.

Prenatal Development

(pages 63–68)

①FOCUS

OBJECTIVES

- Explain fetal development from conception through pregnancy.
- Explain the significance of genetics and its role in fetal development.
- Discuss the importance of healthful living before and during pregnancy.

MOTIVATOR

Write the following on the board for students to work on while attendance is being taken: *Name as many signs of pregnancy as you can that might indicate a female is pregnant.* Assign the Quick Start.

INTRODUCING THE LESSON

Have students share their answers to the Motivator or the Quick Start. Signs of pregnancy may include all of the following:

- A missed menstrual period.
- Nausea. Commonly known as "morning sickness," these bouts can occur throughout the day. Two-thirds of all pregnant females may experience this.
- Enlarged or tender breasts. By the eighth week of pregnancy, in many females, the areolas—the pigmented areas around the nipples—will also have grown darker and larger than normal.

INTRODUCING VOCABULARY

As students read the lesson, have them make a chart listing the terms used to describe a child as it develops from conception until birth, the time period each term includes, and the different characteristics of the developing child in each stage.

②TEACH

Discussing

Have students discuss the myths people tell children about how babies are born. Ask them why they think people have told such stories. **L1**

Discussing

Ask students why it is necessary for the fertilized ovum to travel to the uterus. **L1**

Discussing

Ask students why they think it is important that waste products be removed from the embryo's blood and excreted through the mother's body. **L1**

Class Activity

Ask students to list the structures that help nourish and protect the developing fetus. Have them look in a biology textbook to view these structures. **L1**

Research

Ask students to research how home pregnancy tests work. Have volunteers report to the class on the reliablity of these tests. **L2**

Class Activity

With the class, go over the chart on page 66. You might want to use a ruler to help students more fully understand the dimensions given at various stages. **L1**

Class Activity

Reinforce the concept of dominant and recessive genes by making a chart showing the likelihood of a child being born with blue eyes if: (a) the child inherits a gene for blue eyes from each parent; (b) the child inherits a gene for brown eyes from one parent and a gene for blue eyes from the other. **L1**

Research

Ask students to research differences in the development of multiple embryos in the uterus and share their findings with the class. ⬛2

Research

Ask students to research one of the hereditary diseases discussed in the text or another hereditary disease and share their findings with the class. ⬛2

Discussing

Ask students why prospective parents might consult a genetic counselor. ⬛1

③ ASSESS

EVALUATING THE LESSON

Assign and discuss the Lesson 1 Review on page 68.

Answers to Lesson 1 Review

1. A zygote is a fertilized ovum; it begins dividing, first into two cells, then four, then eight, and so on, and it moves down the fallopian tube to the uterus.
2. The amniotic sac is a fluid-filled sac that surrounds the embryo, protecting it from outside impact and insulating it from temperature changes.
3. The doctor will administer a test and then will perform an internal examination to detect changes in the cervix and the size of the uterus that signify pregnancy.
4. The father's sperm.
5. Genes are units of heredity that determine which traits, or characteristics, offspring inherit from their parents. Inherited genes determine traits such as height, hair color, and skin type.
6. Each parent must have had one gene for blue eyes and one gene for brown eyes; the dominant gene masked the effect of the recessive gene, so their eyes were brown. The child must have received a recessive blue-eye gene from each parent.
7. Possible answer: Genetic counseling helps prospective parents know more about their risk of passing on genetic diseases so that they can make an informed decision about whether to have children. Since most people may not show symptoms of some inherited diseases until later in life, when they may have already

had children, this is especially helpful concerning the risk for these diseases.

Answers to Applying Health Skills

Answers will vary, but students should explain that research has shown that home pregnancy tests yield a high number of false negative results, meaning that the test says a female is not pregnant when she really is. For that reason, if someone thinks she may be pregnant she should have a pregnancy test done by a health care professional.

RETEACHING

Have students prepare a time line that summarizes physical development of the fetus in the uterus throughout pregnancy.

ENRICHMENT

Have students research the history of genetic counseling. Have them report on their findings to the class.

④ CLOSE

Sum up the lesson by discussing with students fertilization and fetal development from conception through birth. The next lesson concentrates on prenatal care of the developing fetus.

Lesson 2

Prenatal Care (pages 69–76)

① FOCUS

OBJECTIVES

- Analyze the harmful effects on the fetus if the mothers uses alcohol, tobacco, and other drugs, as well as environmental hazards such as exposure to lead and radiation.
- Explain the importance of the role of prenatal care and proper nutrition in promoting optimal health for both the baby and the mother.
- Examine how technology has impacted the health status of families by aiding in prenatal diagnosis of certain conditions.

MOTIVATOR

Write the following on the board for students to work on while attendance is being taken: *Why is it important for a female to learn about proper prenatal care as soon as she thinks she might be pregnant?* Assign the Quick Start.

INTRODUCING THE LESSON

Have students share their answers from the Motivator or the Quick Start. Point out that it is important that the mother take care of the developing fetus to help ensure that the baby will be born healthy.

INTRODUCING VOCABULARY

In the last lesson, students learned that the protective sac surrounding the embryo is called the *amniotic sac.* Inform students that *centesis* comes from the Greek, meaning "to puncture." Have students write their own definition of the word *amniocentesis.* Have them check their definition in the Glossary/Glosario.

 TEACH

Discussing

Have students discuss how changes brought on by pregnancy might affect the physical, mental/emotional, and social health of the mother. **L1**

Discussing

Have students think of strategies to help a pregnant female deal with the changes she is experiencing. **L1**

Research

Have students work in groups to research and learn about the services and classes your community offers expectant parents. **L2**

Analyzing

Divide the class into two groups. Ask them to debate the issue of responsibility regarding fetal exposure to drugs and alcohol. For example, should females be held accountable for damage to a fetus caused by drug use? Should bartenders be required by law to withhold alcoholic beverages from females who are obviously pregnant? **L1**

Research

Have students conduct research on the health risks and problems associated with low birth weight. Let volunteers share their findings with the class. **L2**

Class Activity

Ask students to examine the chart on "The Effects of STDs to the Fetus." Have students work in small groups. Assign each group one of the STDs in the chart. Have them research more about the symptoms, treatment, and effects of the STD on infected persons. Allow time for groups to present their information to the class. **L2**

Discussing

Ask students to discuss the reasons why parents might or might not want to know the sex of their baby before it is born. **L1**

Research

Have students contact birth defect prevention organizations (such as the March of Dimes), or look for their Web sites, to learn more about programs for fighting birth defects. **L2**

Research

Have students work in small groups to choose a birth defect and research its causes and treatments, if any. Have groups compile their findings and create an informative booklet on birth defects. **L2**

ASSESS

EVALUATING THE LESSON

Assign and discuss the Lesson 2 Review on page 76.

Answers to Lesson 2 Review

1. See answers under the head "Characteristics of a Pregnancy," subheads "First Trimester," "Second Trimester," and "Third Trimester."
2. Any substance taken in by the mother can be transferred to the fetus through the placenta. Harmful substances cause low birth weight, fetal alcohol syndrome, and other complications.
3. It is a condition of physical, mental, and behavioral abnormalities that can result when a pregnant female drinks alcohol.
4. amniocentesis and chorionic villus sampling
5. Possible answer: Prenatal care can help a

pregnant female make healthy choices about diet, exercise, and avoiding harmful substances. Prenatal care also monitors the health of both the mother and the developing fetus throughout the pregnancy, so that any medical complications can be dealt with should they arise.

6. Development of medical technologies including ultrasound, amniocentesis, and chorionic villus sampling helps doctors and parents monitor fetal development and respond to abnormalities or complications.

Answers to Applying Health Skills

Answers will vary, but students should explain to the sister why alcohol is harmful and should offer refusal strategies such as: say "no" in a firm voice, repeat yourself if necessary, use appropriate body language, suggest an alternative, leave if necessary.

RETEACHING

Have students reread the sections "Medical Complications" and "Dangers to the Fetus" (page 72). Ask them to name the factors over which they have control. Have them explain what steps can be taken to avoid problems during pregnancy.

ENRICHMENT

Have students research fetal alcohol syndrome and report their findings to the class.

 CLOSE

Sum up the lesson by asking students to discuss the role of good prenatal care in a healthy pregnancy and child. The next lesson focuses on childbirth.

Lesson 3

Childbirth (pages 77–80)

 FOCUS

OBJECTIVES

- Identify and explain the stages of labor.
- Explain how breastfeeding promotes optimal health for the baby.

MOTIVATOR

Write the following on the board for students to work on while attendance is being taken: *Look up the definition of* cesarean *in the dictionary.* Assign the Quick Start.

INTRODUCING THE LESSON

Have students share their answers from the Motivator or Quick Start activities. Explain that the word *cesarean* came from the Roman emperor Julius Caesar, who was supposedly born by cesarean section. Have students compare the dictionary definition with that in the Glossary/Glosario.

INTRODUCING VOCABULARY

Tell students that the word *labor* is used to describe many types of physical and mental work. Ask students why they think this word is also used for childbirth.

② TEACH

Discussing

Have students discuss the purpose of the Apgar assessment. How are the scores interpreted? **L1**

Guest Speaker

Invite a childbirth instructor from the community to describe the birth process and the different birthing methods, and to tell how the mother may cope with the pain associated with childbirth. **L1**

Research

Ask students to research different birthing methods and share what they find with the class. **L2**

Discussing

Ask students to list what items new parents need to help take care of their baby. Encourage them to find out about the costs of these items. **L1**

Research

Have students research the ways a father-to-be participates in the prenatal care and delivery of his child. **L2**

Using the Feature

Real-Life Application

ANALYZING INFLUENCES

As students examine the trends, point out the decline in teen pregnancies since 1970. Ask: What factors may have influenced the decline in the number of pregnancies over the last 3 decades?

Discussing

Ask students to discuss why some mothers choose not to have any pain medication when they give birth. **L1**

Research

Have students research the increase in cesarean deliveries over the past several decades and write a brief report summarizing their findings. **L2**

Research

Ask students to contact birthing centers in your community, or research their Web sites, to learn about the types of services they offer. **L2**

③ ASSESS

EVALUATING THE LESSON

Assign and discuss the Lesson 3 Review on page 80.

Answers to Lesson 3 Review

1. First Stage: Contractions open (or dilate) the cervix to a diameter of about 4 inches (10 cm), amniotic sac usually ruptures; Second Stage: begins when the cervix is fully dilated, the mother feels an urge to push; pushing and contractions force the baby through the cervix, into the vagina, and out through the vaginal opening; Third Stage: contractions separate the placenta from the uterine wall and expel it out of the body through the vagina.
2. An episiotomy is an incision made from the vagina toward the anus to enlarge the opening for delivery of a baby. It is used to prevent the tissues around the vaginal opening from tearing.

3. A cesarean birth is a method of childbirth in which a surgical incision is made through the abdominal wall and uterus and the baby is lifted out.
4. The goal is to make the experience of labor and delivery less mysterious and as painless as possible.
5. Infants who are breastfed receive antibodies from their mother's colostrum and breast milk, so they have fewer illnesses. They have an easier time digesting colostrum and breast milk than formula, they receive ideal nutrition, and they do not experience allergic reactions. They don't have to wait for breast milk to be prepared or warmed—it's always ready.
6. The expectant mother and the coach will know what to expect during labor and delivery, and the female will have relaxation and breathing techniques to cope with the pain of labor and help her have a medication-free delivery if that is her goal.

Answer to Applying Health Skills

Possible answer: Stress could cause responses in the body, such as increasing blood pressure, that would not be helpful during pregnancy or labor and delivery. She could use stress-management techniques such as knowing how and when to relax, keeping a positive outlook, being physically active, and managing her time to deal with problems throughout her pregnancy.

RETEACHING

Have students (male and female) write a short essay on what it would be like to either experience or be with someone going through the three stages of labor.

ENRICHMENT

Have students do a study of midwifery—the use of midwives in childbirth. What is involved? How often are midwives used in the United States? What percentage of these are women? How often are midwives used in other parts of the world? What kind of training is required? In what kinds of settings do midwives usually practice? What might be the benefits and drawbacks of using a midwife during childbirth?

4 CLOSE

Sum up the lesson and chapter by asking students to name the many factors influencing the outcome of each birth.

Chapter 5 Review Answers

Assign and discuss the Chapter 5 Review on page 81.

1. The union of a single sperm and an ovum. Pregnancy begins with fertilization.
2. At the end of the third month.
3. The couples' family histories can be mapped, and medical tests can be run to identify genetic or biochemical markers for some hereditary diseases.
4. The mother's abdomen swells, she can detect fetal movements, her appetite and blood volume increase, any morning sickness usually subsides. Hormonal shifts may cause forgetfulness; some females may have trouble concentrating. Weight gain changes the female's center of gravity and loosens ligaments, causing some females to feel clumsy.
5. Babies born to smokers can have lower birth weights, heart and brain abnormalities, and cleft lip and palate. Maternal smoking is also linked to higher fetal and infant mortality rates, and SIDS.
6. To assess fetal position or evaluate development.
7. There are more than 4,000 known birth defects. They can be caused by abnormal genes or environmental factors.
8. When the cervix is fully dilated, the mother feels an urge to push. She uses muscles to aid the contractions in moving the baby's head through the cervix and into the vagina. When the baby's head crowns, the mother continues to push until the entire baby is delivered. This stage usually lasts from $1/2$ hour to 2 hours.
9. Parents learn what to expect at each stage of labor and delivery. A father, close friend, or relative learns to play the role of coach, and mothers learn relaxation and breathing techniques to cope with the pain of labor and possibly to have a medication-free delivery.
10. A birthing center is a facility that has homelike settings, is separate from a hospital, and offers medication-free births.
11. The placenta, which forms along the lining of the uterus, transfers oxygen and nutrients to the embryo, then the fetus, via the umbilical cord.
12. The doctor will likely suspect preeclampsia. Other symptoms that would confirm this diagnosis are severe swelling from water retention, and/or protein in the urine.
13. Answers will vary, but students may take into account their feelings about the risk of miscarriage, the strain of waiting and not knowing the results until the baby is born.
14. A doctor may schedule a cesarean if the baby is not positioned correctly, if the mother's pelvic structure makes a vaginal delivery dangerous or impossible, or if the mother has an STD that could be transmitted during a vaginal delivery.
15. Pamphlets will vary. Students should provide as many reasons as possible.
16. Answers will vary, but students should communicate as much information as possible about healthful behaviors during pregnancy and labor and delivery.

BEYOND the Classroom

Encourage students to participate in activities that involve parents and the community. Answers will vary.

Lesson 1

Contraception (pages 83–91)

 FOCUS

OBJECTIVES

- Analyze the effectiveness and ineffectiveness of various contraceptive methods and the role they play in the prevention of pregnancy and STDs.
- Analyze the importance of abstinence from sexual activity as the preferred choice of behavior for unmarried persons of school age.
- Discuss abstinence from sexual activity as the only 100 percent effective method of preventing pregnancy and STDs, including HIV/AIDS.

MOTIVATOR

Write the following on the board for students to work on while attendance is being taken: *List some methods of pregnancy prevention.* Assign the Quick Start.

INTRODUCING THE LESSON

Have students share pregnancy prevention methods they noted for the Motivator. Ask class members if each of the methods mentioned is a myth or a proven scientific method. Explain that in this lesson students will examine different methods of pregnancy prevention.

INTRODUCING VOCABULARY

Ask students to look up the root *-ectomy* (surgical removal) and the word *ligation* (something that binds or is tied) in the dictionary. Then ask them what they think the terms *vasectomy* and *tubal ligation* mean.

② TEACH

Discussing

Discuss why misconceptions about pregnancy prevention are so common. Discuss the bulleted list in the "Facts About Pregnancy Prevention" section and ask students why some people might believe the opposite of these are true. **L1**

Cooperative Learning

Divide the class into two groups. Ask each group to decide who is responsible for birth control, the male or the female. Tell the groups to state at least three reasons for their choice. Ask each group to designate a spokesperson to read their answers. Encourage students to discuss the reasons. Finish the activity by telling the students that responsible adult couples share responsibility for birth control. **L2**

Research

Ask students to research the history of one form of birth control discussed in this lesson. Ask them to find out where and when it was first used and how it has changed over the years. **L2**

Class Activity

Ask students to list the advantages and disadvantages of the various forms of birth control discussed in this lesson. **L1**

Discussing

Ask students how practicing abstinence to eliminate concerns about unplanned pregnancy or a sexually transmitted disease might affect a teen's mental and emotional health. **L1**

③ ASSESS

EVALUATING THE LESSON

Assign and discuss the Lesson 1 Review on page 91.

Answers to Lesson 1 Review

1. Any three of the following: the male or female condom, contraceptive foams, contraceptive jellies, contraceptive creams, contraceptive suppositories, FAMs, and abstinence.
2. The male condom must be unrolled onto the erect penis, keeping a space between the tip of the penis and the end of the condom, before there's any contact with the vagina. As soon as ejaculation occurs, and while holding the condom in place, the penis must be removed from the vagina. Condoms must never be used with petroleum-based products, stored in a hot place, or reused.
3. Any four of the following: nausea, breast tenderness, weight gain, mood swings, breakthrough bleeding.
4. Sterilization is a surgical procedure that makes a male or female incapable of reproducing. The procedure for males is a vasectomy; for females, it is a tubal ligation.
5. One: abstinence; two: the pill; three: male condom; four: diaphragm; five: spermicide.
6. Only abstinence offers total protection against STDs; condoms provide some protection.

Answer to Applying Health Skills

Posters will vary.

RETEACHING

Have students make a chart of prescription and nonprescription contraceptive methods.

ENRICHMENT

Have students prepare speeches advocating abstinence for their peers.

CLOSE

Sum up the lesson by asking students to explain the role of abstinence in avoiding pregnancy or STDs. Remind students that abstinence is the only 100 percent effective method to prevent pregnancy.

Lesson 2

Concerns About Sexuality

(pages 92–95)

FOCUS

OBJECTIVES

- Explain why some people masturbate.
- Describe myths regarding sexual orientation and discuss how to show consideration and respect toward others.
- Distinguish between spontaneous and induced abortion.

MOTIVATOR

Have students work on the following while attendance is being taken: *List two myths about human sexuality issues.* Assign the Quick Start.

INTRODUCING THE LESSON

Have students share their answers from the Motivator or the Quick Start. Explain that in this lesson, they will learn about masturbation, sexual orientation, and abortion.

INTRODUCING VOCABULARY

Have students look up the vocabulary words in the dictionary and compare the meanings with those found in the Glossary/Glosario.

2 TEACH

Discussing

Ask students for reasons why some people might think masturbation is inappropriate. **L1**

Research

Ask students to research the genetic or the chemical environmental theories on the causes of homosexuality. **L2**

Discussing

Ask students what they would say to a friend who thinks he or she might be gay because he or she is not interested in members of the opposite gender. **L2**

Discussing

Have students discuss why induced abortion is a controversial subject. **L1**

Research

Ask students to find articles relating to an election campaign where the candidate discusses his or her views of abortion. Have them summarize the politician's views and explain why politicians often state their views on abortion. **L2**

③ ASSESS

EVALUATING THE LESSON

Assign and discuss the Lesson 2 Review on page 95.

Answers to Lesson 2 Review

1. A homosexual is someone who is sexually attracted to people of the same gender. A heterosexual is someone who is sexually attracted to people of the opposite gender.
2. A stereotype is an idea or image held about a group of people that represents a prejudiced attitude, an oversimplified opinion, or uninformed judgment.
3. Some research suggests that there is a genetic component or different chemical environment during fetal development or a different balance of hormones at birth. Some studies also point to influences in the home or society during a child's formative years.
4. The two types of abortion are spontaneous abortion or miscarriage, which is the spontaneous end of a pregnancy from natural causes; and induced abortion, which is a medically terminated pregnancy.
5. Possible answer: Stereotypes can harm people because they are based on the way people look or behave, and they result in people being incorrectly labeled instead of being shown consideration and respect.
6. Answers will vary, but may include that people have strong viewpoints about induced abortion because it purposefully ends a pregnancy.

Answer to Applying Health Skills

Paragraphs will differ but should reflect an understanding of myths and stereotypes surrounding homosexuality.

RETEACHING

Ask students to summarize why they think each of the subjects in this lesson is so controversial.

ENRICHMENT

Have students select an option for dealing with an unplanned pregnancy. Students should research this option and write a paper that describes the consideration and impact of choosing this option on everyone involved. If appropriate, have volunteers share their papers with the class.

④ CLOSE

Sum up the lesson by stating that there are many controversial issues surrounding the topic of sexuality, and everyone needs not agree.

Lesson 3

Sexual Abuse and Violence

(pages 96–100)

① FOCUS

OBJECTIVES

- Analyze issues surrounding sexual abuse and incest.
- Describe situations that can lead to acquaintance rape and date rape.
- Analyze the importance of healthy strategies that prevent physical, sexual, and emotional abuse, including date rape.

MOTIVATOR

Write the following on the board for students to work on while attendance is being taken: *What associations come to mind when you see or hear the word rape? Do you know why you have these associations?* Assign the Quick Start.

INTRODUCING THE LESSON

Have students share their responses to the Motivator or Quick Start activities. Explain that people sometimes think that rape only happens between strangers or that you can identify a rapist by the way he looks. Tell them that in this lesson, they will learn that rape is any forced sexual contact.

INTRODUCING VOCABULARY

Point out to students that there are three vocabulary terms in this lesson using the word *rape*. Ask them to write what they think are the differences between the three words, and then check the Glossary/Glosario to see how they are defined.

②TEACH

Class Activity

Have students put together a list of local agencies that assist victims of sexual assault or sexual abuse. See that each student has a copy of the list and understands the function of each agency. **L1**

Discussing

Ask students what they should do if they suspected a friend was being sexually abused. **L1**

Guest Speaker

Invite a speaker from a rape crisis center to speak to the class. Before the speaker's visit, have the class make a list of questions they want to ask. **L1**

Discussing

Ask students to discuss why a victim of sexual abuse may find it difficult to report the crime. **L1**

Class Activity

Review the "Protecting Yourself Against Rape" section of the lesson. Ask students to make a list of other ways to protect against rape (for example, to be wary of meeting people on the Internet). **L1**

Using the Feature

DECISION MAKING

Have the class brainstorm a list of Carrie's options. Then ask volunteers to describe in their own words how they would apply the decision-making steps to Carrie's situation.

Research

Have students find current articles about rape cases in which the assailant was convicted. Tell students to find out what sentences were given to those found guilty. Have students compare their findings with those of the rest of the class. **L2**

③ASSESS

EVALUATING THE LESSON

Assign and discuss the Lesson 3 Review on page 100.

Answers to Lesson 3 Review

1. Sexual abuse is any sexual contact that is physically or emotionally forced on a person.
2. A victim of sexual abuse or incest may remain silent about the abuse out of fear, loyalty, or obedience; some victims may believe that they caused the abuse or that they were at fault because they did not resist.
3. The first and most important step a victim of sexual abuse can take is to tell someone about the abuse.
4. Any three of the following: know the person you are going out with and learn about his or her friends and reputation; do not go on blind dates alone; go on group dates the first few times you're out with a new person; do not go to isolated places on a date; tell someone at home where you will be and when you plan to return; take money with you and a cell phone if you have one; do not use drugs or alcohol, and leave immediately if your date uses them.
5. These actions can remove evidence the police will need.
6. Incest is a specific type of sexual abuse that occurs when the sexual abuser is related to the victim.
7. Situations will vary, but students should include some of the information under the head "Protecting Yourself Against Rape" in their suggestions.

Answer to Applying Health Skills

Pamphlets will vary but should list and illustrate many of the guidelines discussed in the lesson.

RETEACHING

Have students explain the importance of immediately reporting a rape to the authorities.

ENRICHMENT

Ask students to research statistics on rape victims. Ask them to find out the percentages of rape victims by gender and age.

CLOSE

Sum up the lesson by asking volunteers to summarize what they have learned about ways young people can protect themselves against sexual abuse.

Chapter 6 Review Answers

Assign and discuss the Chapter 6 Review on page 101.

1. Douching may push sperm farther into the vagina, making fertilization more likely.
2. Withdrawal is the male's removal of the penis from the vagina before ejaculation; it is not an effective method of preventing pregnancy.
3. A contraceptive suppository is inserted into the vagina with an applicator; it takes about 15 minutes to dissolve and release its spermicide. A contraceptive suppository must not be inserted more than 30 minutes before intercourse if it is to effectively kill sperm.
4. They are the basal body temperature method and the cervical mucus method.
5. Any three of the following: birth control pills, diaphragm, cervical cap, or contraceptive implants.
6. Oral contraceptives are hormone pills that, taken correctly, make changes in the female body that prevent pregnancy.
7. A contraceptive implant provides protection from pregnancy for about five years.
8. Spontaneous abortion or miscarriage.
9. Rape is sexual intercourse through force or threat of force.
10. Acquaintance rape is rape by someone the victim knows, whereas date rape is rape by someone the victim is dating.
11. Answers will vary, but students might suggest that they could talk to a trusted adult such as a teacher or a doctor, or they could consult reference material from the library or reliable Internet sites.
12. During a vasectomy, each vas deferens is cut and sealed. The procedure takes about 20 minutes and involves using a local anesthetic. Most males can resume normal activities the following day. It is not immediately effective; a male's semen will not be totally free of sperm until 15 to 20 ejaculations have occurred after surgery. The procedure is 99.9 percent effective. In a tubal ligation, the fallopian tubes are cut and tied or clamped to prevent sperm from reaching the ova. The procedure requires a hospital stay. Complications following surgery may include cramps, heavier periods, breakthrough bleeding, and pelvic pain. Tubal ligation is 99.5 percent effective.
13. Answers will vary, but students should include the health consequences of sexual activity before marriage.
14. Answers will vary, but students may say it happens because they trust the people who give them the false information.
15. Answers will vary, but may include that in-depth counseling can give an abuser insight into the problem.
16. Students' directories should provide comprehensive contact information.
17. Answers will vary, but will probably include the idea that movie characters might influence teens to engage in high-risk sexual behaviors.

Encourage students to participate in activities that involve parents and the community.

- Discussions should include the information presented in Lesson 3.
- Answers will vary.

Lesson 1

Common Sexually Transmitted Infections (pages 103–109)

① FOCUS

OBJECTIVES

- Describe the relationship between high-risk behaviors and the risk of contracting a sexually transmitted disease.
- Recognize and discuss abstinence from sexual activity as the only method that is 100 percent effective in preventing sexually transmitted diseases and infections.
- Develop and identify strategies to prevent the spread of sexually transmitted diseases.

MOTIVATOR

Write the following on the board for students to work on while attendance is being taken: *List the common symptoms of STDs.* Assign the Quick Start.

INTRODUCING THE LESSON

Have students share their responses to the Motivator or Quick Start. Tell students they will learn more about sexually transmitted diseases, their symptoms, and treatments in this chapter.

INTRODUCING VOCABULARY

Ask students to look at the vocabulary list and note any terms they have heard of before. Have them look these words up in the Glossary/Glosario to see how they are defined. Point out to students the reason the CDC has used the term "sexually transmitted infection" in place of "sexually transmitted disease" is because a person can be infected, and be infectious, without necessarily having the disease. Experts also feel people may be more likely to seek testing treatment for an infection.

② TEACH

Discussing

Ask students why they think STDs are on the rise despite all the information available on how to prevent them. **L1**

Discussing

Have students discuss why having an STD might affect the mental and emotional health of a teen. How might it interfere with their goals for the future? **L1**

Guest Speaker

Invite a health care professional from your local health department to speak about STDs. Have each student prepare at least three questions to ask the speaker. **L1**

Class Activity

Ask students to think of strategies to make other teens aware of the benefits of abstinence for avoiding STDs. Ask them to consider what kind of campaigns might be effective in reaching teens. **L1**

Research

Have students research one of the STDs discussed in this lesson. When and where was the disease first reported, and when were treatments or cures discovered? Ask students to share what they learn with the class. **L2**

Using the Feature

> **Health Skills Activity**
>
> **COMMUNICATION**
>
> Before students begin writing their dialogues, have them review the communication skills covered in Chapter 2 of this text. Be sure students describe interaction between Briann and Julia to demonstrate how Julia communicates her message clearly.

Discussing

Have students discuss the importance of sexually active people being tested for STDs even if they are symptom free. Tell them to consider some of the consequences of living with an STD.

③ ASSESS

EVALUATING THE LESSON

Assign and discuss the Lesson 1 Review on page 109.

Answers to Lesson 1 Review

1. Sexually transmitted infections are diseases that spread from person to person through sexual contact. They are difficult to track because some people who have them may not exhibit symptoms and some infected people may not report them.
2. Answers may vary but should include these risk behaviors: engaging in sexual activity without using any barrier protection method; using alcohol and other drugs; being sexually active with more than one person; choosing high-risk partners
3. It is the virus that causes genital warts and can cause cancer in both males and females. Health experts believe that genital HPV infection is the most commonly contracted of all the STDs.
4. Chlamydia, because it often goes undiagnosed since many people have no symptoms
5. Some of the results are: PID; epididymitis; effect on the prostate; scarring inside the urethra; affects the blood or joints, at which point the disease becomes life threatening.
6. Answers will vary, but students should communicate reasons why it is risky to go out with someone who has a reputation for being sexually active.
7. The early symptoms for females often go unnoticed but may involve a burning sensation when urinating and an abnormal vaginal discharge; the early symptoms for males may involve a burning sensation when urinating and a discharge from the penis.

Answer to Applying Health Skills

Pamphlets will vary but should list and illustrate many of the guidelines discussed in the lesson.

.

RETEACHING

Have students make a chart listing the types of STDs they learned about in this lesson, and the symptoms, diagnoses, and treatments of each.

ENRICHMENT

Ask students to find current articles regarding the spread of STDs, especially among teens. Have them share what they learn with the class.

④ CLOSE

Sum up this lesson by asking students to state one fact that they have learned about STDs and their consequences. Tell students they will learn more about STDs in the next lesson.

Lesson 2

Other Sexually Transmitted Infections *(pages 110–114)*

① FOCUS

OBJECTIVES

- Develop and analyze strategies to prevent spreading sexually transmitted diseases.
- Explain the relationship between drug use and unsafe situations that can lead to transmission of STDs.
- Identify, describe, and assess community health services available for prevention and treatment of STDs.
- Analyze the importance and benefits of abstinence in the prevention of STDs.

MOTIVATOR

Write the following on the board for students to work on while you take attendance: *How might a person contract an STD without being sexually active?* Assign the Quick Start.

INTRODUCING THE LESSON

Have students share their responses to the Motivator. (Students may mention sharing needles from injected drug use or body piercing, transmission from mother to baby during pregnancy or childbirth, or contact with infested bed linens or clothing.) Discuss answers to the Quick Start activity. Explain to students that in this lesson they will learn more about other STDs and their treatments.

INTRODUCING VOCABULARY

Tell students that the root *hepat-* comes from the Greek word for "liver" and that the root *-itis* comes from the Latin word for "inflammation." Ask students what they think the word *hepatitis* means. Then ask them what they think *vaginitis* means. Have them check their answers in the Glossary/Glosario.

❷ TEACH

Research

Tell students that there are several different types of hepatitis (A, B, C, D, and E), not all of which are sexually transmitted. Ask students to research one of the hepatitis types and share what they learn about its causes, symptoms, and treatments with the class.

Discussing

Tell students that STDs are often referred to as "silent epidemics" or "silent killers." Ask them to discuss why such labels are applied to STDs. **L1**

Class Activity

Have students write about the serious risk of STDs to teens. The information should be presented in article form, such as for a teen magazine. **L1**

Discussing

Ask students to make a list of what they might say to a friend who is reluctant to see a doctor about a possible STD. **L1**

Research

Ask students to research how sexually transmitted diseases are tracked and by whom. Ask them to consider why it is helpful to track a disease. **L2**

❸ ASSESS

EVALUATING THE LESSON

Assign and discuss the Lesson 2 Review on page 114.

Answers to Lesson 2 Review

1. Hepatitis B is a viral infection that attacks the liver and can cause extreme illness and death. It is transmitted when blood or other body fluids from an infected person enter the body of a person who is not immune to the disease; it is spread through sexual activity, contaminated needles and injected drug use, and through vaginal births.
2. Syphilis is spread by direct contact with a chancre, the painless sore, or with the infectious rash. It is transmitted primarily through sexual activity, but pregnant females can pass the disease to the fetus during pregnancy.
3. Trichomoniasis and bacterial vaginosis.
4. Intense itching is the main symptom.
5. Scabies is an infestation of the skin with microscopic mites.
6. If syphilis is left untreated, it causes severe, sometimes fatal damage to internal organs. Strategies should include being tested and getting treatment for STDs.
7. They can make the decision to practice abstinence.

Answer to Applying Health Skills

Answers will vary, but students should advise the friend to see a doctor first because that painless sore may have been the primary stage of syphilis. Then the students should advise the friend to take all his medication, to follow all of the doctor's orders for treatment, not to engage in sexual activity with anyone, and to be sure to tell all people he has had sexual contact with to seek treatment.

RETEACHING

Have students add to the chart they created for the last lesson *hepatitis B*, *hepatitis C*, *syphilis*, *trichomoniasis*, *bacterial vaginosis*, *pubic lice*, and *scabies*, including the symptoms, diagnoses, and treatments of each.

ENRICHMENT

Tell students that in some states, a couple is required to have their blood tested for STDs and other conditions before a marriage license can be issued. Ask students to research why some states require such tests.

CLOSE

Sum up the lesson by asking students to list the three most important things they learned in this lesson about avoiding STDs.

Chapter 7 Review Answers

Assign and discuss the Chapter 7 Review on page 115.

1. C is true because some STDs have no symptoms in some people, others don't produce symptoms for a long time, and still others have symptoms that go away while the STD remains in the body and can be spread.
2. Abstinence. Abstaining from high-risk behaviors, such as alcohol or drug use and sexual activity before marriage, is the only method that is 100 percent effective in avoiding STDs.
3. Both males and females can get chlamydia.
4. It is a painful infection of the uterus, fallopian tubes, and/or ovaries. Permanent damage to these structures, with severe pelvic pain, infertility, and increased likelihood of ectopic pregnancy, can result.
5. It is most commonly diagnosed by examining genital warts. It is treated by having the genital warts removed by laser or by being frozen, burned, or cut off; or by having an antiviral drug injected into larger warts and/or using other topical treatments. Removal of the warts does not eliminate the virus, however, and the warts often recur.
6. One reason is that once a person has been infected, he or she will always have the disease and can spread it to other people.
7. An infectious rash of nonitchy, rough, red or reddish-brown spots appears on the palms of the hands and the soles of the feet. Flulike symptoms, hair loss, and weight loss can also be present. The rash disappears without treatment.

8. Syphilis is diagnosed by a blood test or by a laboratory examination of material from the primary chancre or the secondary-stage rash.
9. Pubic lice are treated with a special medicated over-the-counter or prescription shampoo.
10. A doctor or public health clinic provides diagnosis and treatment for STDs.
11. STDs can be prevented by making healthy choices and not engaging in sexual activity. There is no effective way to protect against the common cold.
12. Answers will vary, but students might discuss a patient's need for privacy in order to seek treatment and parents' concern for the health of a teen who may have an STD or is engaging in risky behaviors.
13. Answers will vary, but students should suggest that they would advise their friend to seek medical attention.
14. The partners could become infected, as could a baby, if the infected person is female and becomes pregnant. Partners could also infect other people, thus spreading the disease.
15. STDs affect the health of infected individuals and the health of others.
16. Radio announcements will vary.
17. Answers will vary, but students may suggest that teens are not as well informed as adults, that they may engage in risky behaviors, or that they believe they are immune from harm because of their age.

BEYOND *the* **Classroom**

Encourage students to participate in activities that involve parents and the community.

- Encourage students to discuss these issues with parents or guardians.
- Reports will vary depending on the STD students choose to research.

Lesson 1

What Is HIV/AIDS?

(pages 117–121)

OBJECTIVES

- Identify the stages and symptoms of HIV infection and AIDS.
- Explain the relationship between risky behaviors, unsafe situations, and the transmission of HIV.
- Explain why abstinence from alcohol, drugs, and sexual activity is the only 100 percent effective method of preventing HIV infection.

MOTIVATOR

Write the following on the board for students to work on while attendance is being taken: *How is HIV spread? How is HIV not spread?* Assign the Quick Start.

INTRODUCING THE LESSON

Have students share their answers to the Motivator or the Quick Start activities. Tell students that in this lesson they will learn the ways HIV can be spread. They will also learn about ways HIV is not spread.

INTRODUCING VOCABULARY

Tell students that the word *syndrome* comes from the Greek words *syn-*, meaning "with" or "together with" and *dramein*, meaning "to run." Ask students to explain why they think AIDS is a syndrome.

②TEACH

Discussing

Emphasize that AIDS is caused by a virus called HIV. Have students identify other diseases caused by a virus, such as polio, chicken pox, measles, herpes, influenza, mononucleosis, mumps, rabies, and the common cold. Point out that many of these diseases can be prevented through immunizations. Tell students that isolating HIV was the first step in the ongoing process of finding a way to stop AIDS. **L1**

Research

Have students research more about the origins of HIV. Have them share their findings with the class. **L2**

Class Activity

Ask students to list five safe, entertaining activities they have participated in over the last week that offered no risk of contracting HIV. Have volunteers read activities from their lists and write these on the board under the heading "No-Risk Behaviors." You might also want to use this heading for a bulletin board that students can decorate with pictures cut out from magazines or newspapers. **L1**

Discussing

Review each of the ways HIV is spread. Have students discuss how HIV can enter the blood. Have students reread the section "How HIV Is Transmitted." Then add that cuts in the skin of the penis and on the vaginal wall can be so tiny that they do not bleed visibly. Therefore, most people are unaware of them. Ask students why these cuts are dangerous. **L1**

Discussing

Have students debate the following statement: "An individual infected with HIV should be allowed to play contact sports." Encourage students to support their positions with factual information from the lesson about HIV transmission and how it might impact such a situation. **L1**

Guest Speaker

Invite a representative from the local health department to speak about HIV transmission and risk behaviors. Have each student prepare a brief essay describing what he or she learned from the speaker. **L1**

Discussing

Have students explain, using their own words, the meaning of the term *AIDS-opportunistic illness* (an illness that would not harm a person with a healthy immune system; takes advantage of the weaknesses in the immune system caused by HIV). Explain the statement: "A person does not die from AIDS but from another disease or opportunistic illness." (HIV destroys the immune system but the virus itself does not cause death. The damage to the immune system leaves the body with no way to fight off AIDS-opportunistic illnesses, which then prove fatal.) **L1**

③ ASSESS

EVALUATING THE LESSON

Assign and discuss the Lesson 1 Review on page 121.

Answers to Lesson 1 Review

1. AIDS is a fatal disorder with no fully effective treatment or known cure. AIDS is the final stage of infection with the human immunodeficiency virus (HIV), a virus that attacks the immune system.
2. This stage lasts for a span of years. The virus is largely confined to the lymph nodes, where it invades and takes over or destroys T-helper cells. There are no outward signs of the infection—the person looks and feels healthy.
3. The virus is borne in body fluids such as blood, semen, vaginal secretions, and breast milk. It is transmitted by activities or risk behaviors that cause a person to come in contact with these fluids from an infected person if there are breaks in the skin at the point of contact for the uninfected person.
4. No, only teens who are or have been sexually active and/or use or have used drugs, especially injection drugs, are at serious risk for HIV/AIDS.
5. Answers will vary.
6. Answers will vary but should include

increasing numbers of people affected, lack of a cure, effects on victims and their families, and costs for health care.

Answer to Applying Health Skills

Posters will vary, but should include strategies to avoid high-risk behaviors.

RETEACHING

Have students use each of the vocabulary terms in a written sentence to explain how HIV is transmitted and the effect it has on the body. Have students form groups to share sentences. Discuss any discrepancies.

ENRICHMENT

Have students find information about the spread of HIV in other countries. Have them share their findings with the class.

④ CLOSE

Sum up the lesson by telling students that anyone can get HIV, regardless of race, gender, and sexual orientation. Ask students to explain the ways teens can make responsible decisions about risky behaviors to avoid infection.

Lesson 2

HIV/AIDS Testing and Treatment

(pages 122–127)

① FOCUS

OBJECTIVES

- Describe the tests that are used to diagnose the presence of HIV antibodies.
- Identify the symptoms of HIV infection and AIDS.
- Explain how technology and the use of various drugs and combinations of drugs are used in the treatment of AIDS.
- Identify, describe, and assess support services available in the community for individuals with HIV/AIDS and their families.

MOTIVATOR

Write the following on the board for students to work on while attendance is being taken: *What kinds of care and help might a person infected with HIV/AIDS need?* Assign the Quick Start.

INTRODUCING THE LESSON

Have students share their answers to the Motivator or the Quick Start. Tell students that people with HIV/AIDS need more than just health care. They often need practical help, such as legal and social services, as well as a variety of other community services such as hospice or grief counseling.

INTRODUCING VOCABULARY

Point out that many of the vocabulary terms are the names of diseases. Ask students why they think so many of these names also have shortened forms. (They are long, with many syllables, and might be difficult for people to pronounce and remember. Shortened forms might sound less threatening.)

② TEACH

Discussing

Review the symptoms of HIV infection with the class. Ask students what other conditions besides HIV infection might cause the same symptoms (diseases of the blood, pregnancy, presence of other diseases). Emphasize that whenever symptoms are present for any length of time, a person should visit a health care professional for diagnosis and treatment of whatever is causing the symptoms. **L1**

Research

Have students find out how HIV tests are performed. Ask them to explain which bodily fluids can be tested for HIV. Have students call a local testing facility to find out what type of fluid is tested. **L2**

Class Activity

Have students go to the library and research Elizabeth Glaser, who in 1988 co-founded the Pediatric AIDS Foundation after Elizabeth and her husband, Paul, found out that she and their two children were infected with HIV. Ask students to discuss why children infected with HIV might need different treatment than adults infected with the virus. **L1**

Discussing

Discuss the difference between a cure and a vaccine. (A cure heals those who have contracted a disease. A vaccine immunizes people who have not contracted a disease, preventing them from ever becoming infected.) **L1**

Using the Feature

Real-Life Application

ACCESSING INFORMATION

Point out to students the source of this information on the cost of HIV/AIDS. Ask whether they consider this a reliable source of information. Then have volunteers explain why or why not.

Class Activity

Have students find out what services are available locally for people with HIV/AIDS. Remind students to include testing facilities, health care providers, and legal and counseling services. Ask them to create a chart listing the services with descriptions and contact information. Display the charts in the classroom. **L1**

③ ASSESS

EVALUATING THE LESSON

Assign and discuss the Lesson 2 Review on page 127.

Answers to Lesson 2 Review

1. The tests detect HIV antibodies.
2. He or she should not engage in activities that can transmit HIV until testing at six months after exposure is also negative.
3. It requires that a person be HIV positive *and* have *either* a T-helper cell count below 200 *or* the presence of at least one AIDS-OI.
4. Using a cocktail, or assortment, of drugs helps minimize side effects and prevent HIV from becoming resistant to individual drugs.
5. They provide practical assistance, one-on-one support, crisis counseling, grief counseling, and information dissemination.
6. The EIA test is a screening tool used to detect the presence of antibodies for HIV in the blood. If the results of this test are positive two times, a confirmatory test such as the Western

blot is done. If this test is positive, a person is considered to be infected with HIV.

7. Answers will vary, but may include that individuals can't afford it, don't like the side effects, or don't have enough information about it to get treatment.

Answer to Applying Health Skills

Plans will vary. Students should include descriptions of local services and ways to encourage others to participate.

RETEACHING

Put the following headings on the board: *PCP, KS, CMV*, and *Candidiasis*. Have students list facts about each disease under its heading. If necessary, have students reread the section "Diagnosis of AIDS" to locate the facts.

ENRICHMENT

Have students do research to find out about the Declaration of Commitment on HIV/AIDS issued by the United Nations in 2001. Ask them to write a brief report about the declaration and why the United Nations is involved with HIV/AIDS.

 CLOSE

Sum up the lesson by asking students to list the three most important things they learned about HIV testing and treatment.

Chapter 8 Review Answers

Assign and discuss the Chapter 8 Review on page 128.

1. HIV enters certain cells, including T-helper cells, and reproduces itself. As more cells become infected, more are destroyed and the immune system weakens. The body succumbs to AIDS-opportunistic illnesses.
2. They are illnesses the body could normally fight off if the immune system were healthy.
3. The main way is through unprotected sexual activity with an infected partner.
4. Any three of the following: through shaking hands, touching, or hugging; by sharing towels, combs, eating utensils, or bathroom facilities; by coughing or sneezing; by the bites of insects such as mosquitoes.

5. The best methods of prevention of HIV/AIDS involve avoiding risk behaviors—for teens, abstinence from sexual activity before marriage and avoidance of all drug use, especially injection drug use.
6. They are flulike symptoms including fever, headache, fatigue, and swollen lymph nodes. They usually disappear within one to four weeks.
7. HIV can remain in the body for a span of years before symptoms appear.
8. It is a kind of cancer that develops in connective tissues, usually in the skin or in the linings of the mouth, nose, or anus. In more serious cases it involves the lungs, liver, gastrointestinal tract, and lymph nodes.
9. They inhibit HIV from making copies of itself.
10. They are organizations, staffed largely by volunteers, that provide a wide range of essential services to HIV/AIDS patients, their families, and their loved ones.
11. Answers will vary but may include that people only know what they've heard from other people, they have not read scientific or factual articles, or they believe in certain stereotypes that keep them from learning the facts.
12. Answers will vary, but students should provide explanations for their opinions.
13. Answers will vary, but students should provide explanations for their opinions.
14. The person should avoid behaviors known to transmit HIV for six months and be retested.

 BEYOND *the* Classroom

Encourage students to participate in activities that involve parents and the community.

- Discussions may include issues of increased risk of contracting HIV infection, public health, and confidentiality.
- Answers will vary but should include saying "no" firmly and leaving.

Human Sexuality

Mary Bronson Merki, Ph.D.

New York, New York   Columbus, Ohio   Chicago, Illinois   Peoria, Illinois   Woodland Hills, California

About the Author

Mary Bronson Merki, Ph.D., has taught health education in grades K–12, as well as health education methods classes at the undergraduate and graduate levels. As Health Education Specialist for the Dallas School District, Dr. Merki developed and implemented a district-wide health education program, *Skills for Living,* which was used as a model by the state education agency. She also helped develop and implement the district's Human Growth, Development, and Sexuality program, which won the National PTA's Excellence in Education Award. Dr. Merki has assisted school districts throughout the country in developing local health education programs. In 1992 and 1998, she was selected as Teacher of the Year by her peers. In 1996 and again in 2000, she was recognized in *Who's Who Among American Teachers*. She is also the author of Glencoe's *Teen Health* textbook series.

The McGraw-Hill Companies

Send all inquiries to:
Glencoe/McGraw-Hill
21600 Oxnard Street, Suite 500
Woodland Hills, CA 91367

ISBN 0-07-830945-X (Student Edition)
ISBN 0-07-830946-8 (Teacher Annotated Edition)

Printed in the United States of America

3 4 5 6 7 8 9 073 08 07 06 05

Table of Contents

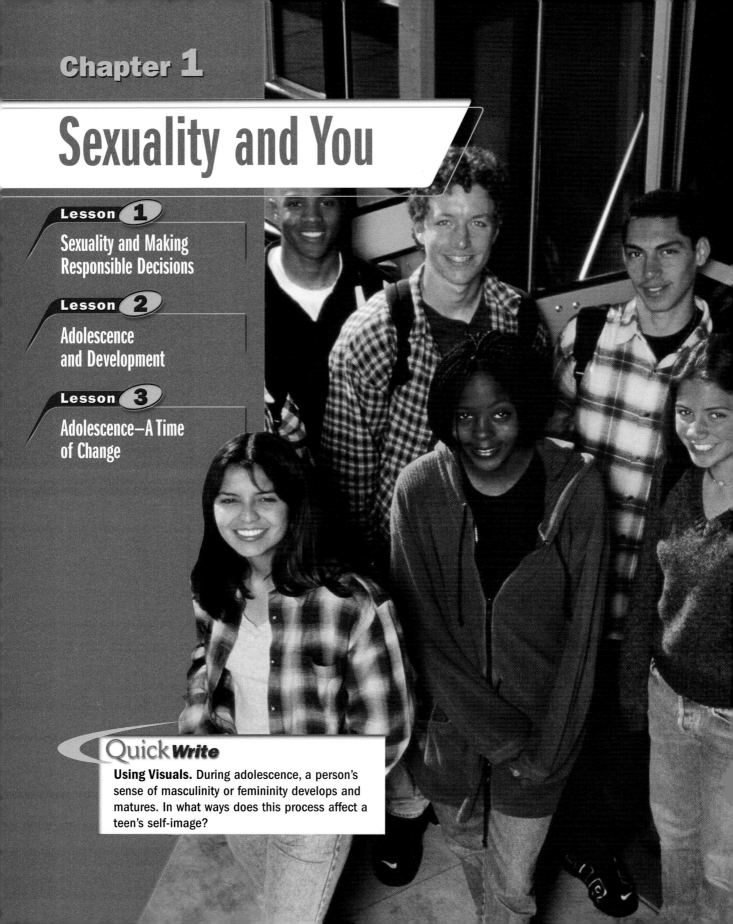

Chapter 1

Sexuality and You

Quick *Write*

Using Visuals. During adolescence, a person's sense of masculinity or femininity develops and matures. In what ways does this process affect a teen's self-image?

Sexuality and Making Responsible Decisions

VOCABULARY

sexuality
self-concept
goal

YOU'LL LEARN TO

- Explain how sexuality develops.

- Identify and appraise the physical, mental/emotional, and social changes that occur during adolescence.

- Identify decision-making skills that promote individual, family, and community health.

- Summarize the advantages of seeking advice and feedback when making healthful decisions.

QUICK START People make decisions that affect their health every day. Write down a decision that you recently made that concerns your physical, mental/emotional, or social health. Then explain how and why you made that decision.

A common theme in books, magazines, and movies, and on the Internet is the use of sexual messages. Advertisers often try to use sexual messages to help them sell their products. Even though information and promotion of sex seems to be everywhere, some people feel uncomfortable talking about it. To them, sex is a private matter, and they don't talk about it or ask questions about it.

Questions About Sexuality

So how do people know they have all the facts? It's important to have factual information about sexuality issues to help you understand your growth and development. This book will address some important issues about sexuality and help you make responsible decisions that protect your health and prevent diseases.

DISCUSS. Ask students to talk about some of the pressures, in addition to media, that teens may experience when making decisions about sexuality issues.

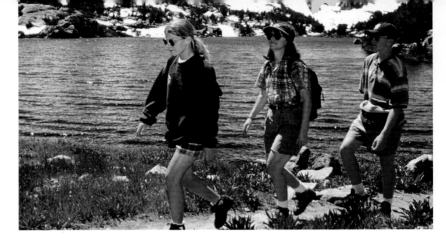

Regular physical activity is one of the keys to good physical health. *What physical activities do you enjoy?*

Strategies for Meeting Emotional Needs in Healthy Ways

For good mental/emotional health:

▶ Focus on recognizing the things you do well and be willing to improve on areas that can use some attention and effort.

▶ Pay attention to your feelings and listen to your body. Be aware of your emotional ups and downs and find the support you need to deal with emotional change.

▶ Discover interests beyond your school day by getting involved in drama, ceramics, martial arts, or local history. An added benefit to expanding your knowledge is making new friends who share your interests.

▶ Reach out to help people in need in your community, such as older adults, children, and individuals who need assistance. When you volunteer your time and talents, you will feel good about yourself because you are making a contribution to society.

Your Sexuality and Health

Your **sexuality** refers to *everything about you as a male or female.* The way you act, your personality, how you feel about yourself because you are male or female—all of these are part of your sexual identity. Learning about sexuality is an ongoing process that changes as you live, grow, and develop. Your sexuality is an integral part of your health and well-being, including your physical, mental/emotional, and social health.

Physical Health

Good physical health means that you have enough energy to perform the activities of daily life and to cope with everyday stresses and challenges. When you are in good physical health, your body can resist diseases and you are more able to protect yourself from injury. Being physically healthy involves

▶ getting at least eight hours of sleep each night.

▶ eating nutritious meals.

▶ being physically active on a regular basis.

▶ drinking eight 8-ounce glasses of water each day.

▶ avoiding harmful substances, such as tobacco, alcohol, and other drugs.

It is equally important to take care of your reproductive system by practicing healthful behaviors. Practice good hygiene, get regular physical exams, and make responsible decisions that protect against unplanned pregnancy and sexually transmitted diseases.

Mental and Emotional Health

Mental and emotional health relate to how well you adjust and adapt to your surroundings. People with good mental health generally feel good about themselves and tend to be self-confident. They can relate well to other people and are able to cope with life's daily demands. They are tuned in to their feelings and can express themselves in considerate and appropriate ways. They have developed emotional maturity, critical-thinking skills, and are able to use reason.

All individuals need to feel that they are important to other people and that they belong to a group. People need to love and be loved, and to feel they have personal value or worth. As part of this, people have a need to achieve, to make a contribution, and to be recognized.

There is a strong relationship between good mental health and a good **self-concept**, or *the mental image you have about yourself*. Beginning in infancy, you receive a variety of signals from people around you that influence how you see yourself. Self-concept is probably the single most important factor influencing what you do. For example, your self-concept influences your ability to make healthy choices. People who respect themselves are more likely to take better care of themselves than people with low self-concepts.

People who do not come from a nurturing or encouraging environment may engage in high-risk behaviors such as using alcohol or drugs. The more protective factors in a person's life, the less likely that person is to seek love and approval by becoming involved in high-risk behaviors, such as engaging in sexual activity before marriage or the use of alcohol, tobacco, and other drugs. Learning to communicate well and to express, understand, and responsibly handle sexual feelings enhances self-concept along with mental and emotional health.

Social Health

Adolescence is a time of tremendous change, not only for your body, mind, and emotions, but also for your relationships. During this period, you often begin to examine your values and beliefs and those of your family. You may compare them to those of friends and society at large and start working to shape your own values and standards of behavior into a personal value system that is your own. As you mature, you can benefit from seeking advice and feedback from parents or trusted adults to help you make healthful decisions. This process helps you begin to build your independent identity for the adult world.

As you progress, your social health also requires an increasing ability to communicate well and share your feelings with others. In connection with your sexuality, social health includes meeting new people, dating, and developing a variety of relationships. All of your relationships will grow and change as you develop your personal value system.

CRITICAL THINKING. Have students consider the relationship between avoiding alcohol and other drugs, and making responsible decisions that protect against unplanned pregnancy and sexually transmitted diseases.

DISCUSS. Ask students whether they think that frequently smiling at and talking to an infant has an impact on the infant's self-concept.

EMPHASIZE. Point out that the values and beliefs of a person's family or other adult caregivers form the basis for that individual's personal value system and standards of behavior.

The messages you receive from others help form your self-concept, the mental image you have of yourself. *What other factors help you to live a healthy life?*

Making Responsible Decisions

As an adolescent, you are continually faced with choices that can have either positive or negative effects on your overall health. The decisions you make in some of these situations can affect your life for years to come. For example, you might find yourself in a situation where alcohol is present. You need to know how to decide what you should do and consider the consequences to your health and safety.

Decisions, especially about your health and sexuality, can be difficult to make. When you are confronted with a difficult decision, it helps to break the decision down into smaller, more manageable steps. This decision-making model can help you act in ways that promote your health, self-esteem, and respect for others. There are six basic steps in making an important decision.

1. **State the situation.** Be sure the problem is clear in your mind. Ask yourself: who is involved, how did the problem develop, and how much time do you have to make a decision?

2. **List the options.** Think of as many ways of solving the problem as you can. Enlist the help of parents, teachers, or trusted friends to get other ideas.

3. **Weigh the possible outcomes.** Consider the consequences of each option, using the word **HELP** as a guide:

   ▶ **H** (Healthful) What health risks, if any, will this option present?

   ▶ **E** (Ethical) Does this choice reflect what you and your family believe is right?

   ▶ **L** (Legal) Does it violate any local, state, or federal laws?

   ▶ **P** (Parental approval) Would your parents or guardians approve of this choice?

4. **Consider values.** Values are the ideas, beliefs, and attitudes about what is important that help guide the way you live. Consider how each option will reflect your values.

5. **Make a decision and act on it.** Put together all the information you have, make a responsible decision, and act.

6. **Evaluate the decision.** After you have made the decision and taken action, examine the consequences of your decision. How did your decision affect your health and the health of others? Were there any unintended consequences? What did you learn that you would apply in the future?

When you are faced with a difficult decision, consider your values and ask yourself how you will ultimately feel about that decision.

DISCUSS. Take the time here to practice the decision-making process. Use a sample student problem and have the class work through each step. It is critical that students practice identifying all possible options and evaluating the consequences of each.

Goal Setting and Healthy Decisions

A **goal** is *something you aim for that takes planning and work.* Goal setting involves making decisions that will help you meet a goal you have set for yourself. When you are faced with decisions affecting your health, such as those dealing with dating, relationships, and sexuality, clear goals for the future will help you to make responsible decisions. These steps will help you reach your goals.

1. **Select a goal and write it down.** Make it specific, realistic, and something that is important to you and your health.

2. **List the steps you will take to reach your goal.** Break your goal into smaller, short-term goals.

3. **Identify sources of help and support.** Sources might include parents or guardians, other family members, friends, peers, or teachers.

4. **Set a reasonable time frame for reaching your goal.** After deciding on a reasonable time, put it in writing.

5. **Evaluate your progress by establishing checkpoints.** Periodically check your progress and make any necessary adjustments that will help you reach your goal.

6. **Reward yourself after achieving your goal.** Choose a reward that is attainable and healthful. Spending time in a favorite activity is more realistic than buying a new stereo.

CRITICAL THINKING. Ask students to give current examples of situations in which they want to set goals for themselves (for example, going to college, completing a difficult course, doing well on a sports team). Have students identify someone who could help them achieve their goals.

▶ Lesson 1 *Review*

LESSON 1 REVIEW ANSWERS ARE FOUND ON PAGE TM10.

Reviewing Facts and Vocabulary

1. Define *sexuality* and discuss how it develops.
2. Identify and appraise three areas of health that are affected by changes during adolescence.
3. Define *self-concept* and explain what influences a teen's self-concept.
4. How can you apply the decision-making process to make responsible decisions?

Thinking Critically

5. **Synthesizing.** Make a list of positive mental and emotional changes that occur during adolescence. Describe two specific skills you can develop to promote good physical, mental, and emotional health for yourself, your family, and community.

6. **Analyzing.** Summarize the advantages of seeking advice and feedback when making healthful decisions. How can a positive self-concept affect decision making? Give two examples.

Applying Health Skills

Goal Setting. Think about an important goal, related to an extra-curricular activity, that you would like to achieve. Use the goal-setting process to map out an action plan for working toward your goal. Which decisions were the easiest to make? Which ones were the most difficult?

Adolescence and Development

YOU'LL LEARN TO

- Identify the developmental tasks of adolescence.

- Demonstrate strategies for communicating needs, wants, and emotions that lead to responsible behaviors.

- Analyze how changes during adolescence lead to an increased ability to demonstrate empathy toward others.

QUICK START Fold a piece of paper evenly into thirds to make three vertical columns. Across the top of the three columns, write *Mental, Emotional,* and *Social.* Under each heading, write how you have changed since childhood in each category. Write as many specific examples as you can.

▲ Although some of the changes that occur during adolescence are physical, many changes affect mental and emotional development.

During adolescence, physical, mental, emotional, and social changes take place in the human body. As an adolescent, you also experience more subtle cognitive changes that cause you to approach problems in new ways. Everyone goes through this in the process of achieving adulthood. **Cognitive** changes are changes *relating to the ability to reason and think out abstract solutions.*

Tasks of Adolescence

Based on the work of Robert Havighurst, a sociologist who specializes in adolescence, there are developmental tasks adolescents must accomplish during their teens and into their twenties. A **developmental task** is *an event that needs to occur during a particular age period for a person to continue his or her growth toward becoming a healthy, mature adult.* These tasks are summarized below:

▶ Adjusting to and accepting a new physical sense of self

▶ Adjusting to new intellectual abilities and new cognitive demands at school

- Developing expanded verbal skills to allow for expression of more complex concepts and needs

- Achieving and managing a masculine or feminine social role and a personal sense of identity

- Establishing adult goals of marriage and/or career

- Establishing emotional and psychological independence from parents

- Forming more mature and stable relationships with peers

- Adopting a personal value system and standards of behavior

- Developing behavioral maturity

Your ability to think on a higher level increases in adolescence. *How have your verbal skills helped you to show maturity?*

Intellectual Development

Until about the age of 12, children think in "concrete" terms, and they believe only what they can see. Consider showing a child two containers that hold exactly the same volume of water but are shaped differently—one container is tall and thin, the other short and wide. If you pour the same amount of water into each container, the child is likely to say that there is more water in the taller container because the water comes up higher in that container. This experiment demonstrates the concrete thinking of the child. As an adolescent, you have bridged that gap between concrete and abstract thought, and now you are capable of more complex thinking.

- **Abstract Thinking.** Abstract thinking allows you to analyze and evaluate information, to better understand cause and effect, to examine consequences, and to draw your own conclusions.

- **Logical Thinking.** Along with abstract thinking comes growth in mental abilities and an ability to use logic to reason things out. In your head, you can go through the steps from point A to point B and figure out possible consequences.

- **Other Higher-Level Thinking.** Your ability to see the finer points of an issue increases, and you are also able to remember more. You may find that you are more willing to consider points of view other than your own.

Developing Responsibility

During adolescence, it is natural to work toward achieving emotional independence from your parents or guardians. As this occurs, you will need to make more decisions on your own and accept the results that come with those decisions. The advanced thinking skills that develop with adolescence will improve your decision-making skills just as your need for them increases. As you make more and more decisions, it is important to remember that *you* are the one responsible for your choices and that the consequences that follow are your responsibility as well.

Health Skills Activity

Decision Making: Dealing with Peer Pressure

Paul and Mike are downtown waiting for a bus after the game on Saturday when Mike's cousin, Steve, drives up.

"Hey, Mike," Steve calls. "Jump in, guys, we'll give you a ride!" Paul notices that Steve and his friends have beers.

Paul says, "It's okay, Mike. The bus will be here in a minute. I think it's safer if we don't ride with them."

Mike turns to look directly at him. "Aw, come on, Paul, it will be fine."

Paul wonders what he should do.

What Would You Do?
Apply the six steps of the decision-making process to Paul's problem.
1. State the situation.
2. List the options.
3. Weigh the possible outcomes.
4. Consider values.
5. Make a decision and act on it.
6. Evaluate the decision.

Developing Mature Relationships

One part of a teen's social development is a growing ability to feel more deeply and consider the needs of other people. This process is crucial to forming more mature peer relationships. As children, most people learn **empathy**, *the ability to feel what others feel, to put yourself in someone else's place.* As an adolescent, you are developing more sensitivity toward others that goes beyond the child's ability to cry when another cries. Your advanced thinking skills allow you to understand the feelings of a friend, and motivate you to want to help him or her resolve whatever it is that is causing distress.

When you demonstrate empathy toward others and offer help, you must always remember to show respect for the other person's feelings, goals, and ideas. Even if you do not share the person's feelings, you can show that you care. Always remember, too, that good friends never urge each other to do something that goes against their beliefs.

Your ability to communicate and express yourself in mature ways will allow you to make responsible decisions in any relationship. When you know how to communicate your feelings, you will be better equipped to avoid unhealthful risk behaviors.

 Becoming more thoughtful of other people is one of the changes that allows teens to form more mature relationships with their peers.

DISCUSS. Ask students to suggest situations in which feeling empathy for a peer might help that person. (For example, if you feel empathy for a classmate who has done poorly on a test, your empathy might lead you to suggest a study session in which you help the other student.)

▶ Lesson 2 Review

LESSON 2 REVIEW ANSWERS ARE FOUND ON PAGE TM12.

Reviewing Facts and Vocabulary

1. Define *developmental task*.
2. Name four developmental tasks for adolescents suggested by sociologist Robert Havighurst.
3. What process is crucial to forming more mature peer relationships and the ability to demonstrate empathy?

Thinking Critically

4. **Evaluating.** Review the list of Robert Havighurst's developmental tasks. Which ones do you think would be the most difficult to attain? Explain your reasoning.
5. **Analyzing.** Explain how changes that occur during adolescence lead to increased cognitive abilities and the ability to communicate needs, wants, and emotions. Provide two examples of ways that a teen might show he or she is developing more complex thinking abilities.

Applying Health Skills

Communication Skills. Write a dialogue in which a teen offers assistance and empathy to a friend who is having a problem. Show how the teen demonstrates empathy and communicates consideration in a respectful way.

Adolescence—A Time of Change

YOU'LL LEARN TO

- Identify and appraise the causes and significance of the physical changes that occur during adolescence.

- Explain the role of hormones during puberty.

- Relate the development of secondary sex characteristics to chemical changes that occur within the body.

QUICK START Suppose you have a younger sister or brother aged 10 or 11 who is the same gender as you are. If your sister or brother asked you what to expect in the way of changes in the next few years, what would you say? Write down your answer, being as specific as you can, and include emotional as well as physical changes.

DISCUSS. Endo- means "within"; exo- means "out." Exocrine glands in the body—tear and oil glands for example—secrete chemicals into ducts that deliver the chemicals to a specific organ or location. Endocrine glands do not have ducts, but release their chemicals directly into the blood. Ask students to consider what advantages there may be in releasing the product of a gland into the blood.

The body is remarkably complex, with organ systems working together to create and regulate growth, change, flexibility, and stability. The nervous system is the primary regulating system of the body; it works closely with the endocrine system to regulate a variety of body functions.

The **endocrine system** is *a body system made up of ductless glands that secrete chemicals called hormones into the blood.* **Hormones** are *chemical substances that regulate the activities of different body cells and organs.* Hormones control the changes that occur during puberty.

Puberty

During adolescence, hormones signal your body to make the changes that occur during puberty. **Puberty** is *the period of growth from physical childhood to physical adulthood when a person begins to develop certain traits of adults of his or her own gender.* Puberty is marked by periods of rapid, uneven physical growth, and all teens go through it at their own pace—a pace that is right for their body. Changes during puberty occur at different times for each individual. The variation in sizes and shapes among people the same age is entirely normal.

Hormones and the Pituitary Gland

Hormones act as chemical stimulators that regulate body functions in three ways.

▶ Hormones stimulate reactions in parts of the body, such as the rush of adrenaline you get in an emergency situation. Your heart races; your mouth gets dry; your palms sweat. You cannot control the secretion of a hormone or your body's reaction to it. Keep this in mind as you learn about other hormonal effects.

▶ During growth periods, hormones produce structural changes in the body, including bone development, maturation of reproductive organs, and development of secondary sex characteristics.

▶ Hormones regulate the rate of metabolism, the rate at which body cells produce energy.

The hormones responsible for changes in your body during puberty are released by the pituitary gland. The **pituitary gland** is *the gland that controls much of the endocrine system.* It is about the size of a pea and is located at the base of the brain. An area of the brain called the hypothalamus stimulates the pituitary to release the necessary hormones. Besides growth hormones, the pituitary gland releases hormones that affect the brain, glands, skin, bones, muscles, and reproductive organs. It also secretes two hormones that are responsible for stimulating maturation of the reproductive organs that produce sex cells. These are the testes in the male and the ovaries in the female. The two hormones are LH (luteinizing hormone) and FSH (follicle-stimulating hormone).

▶ In the male, LH controls the amount of the hormone testosterone produced by the testes, and FSH controls sperm production.

▶ In the female, FSH and LH control the levels of the hormones estrogen and progesterone produced by the ovaries; FSH also causes maturation of ova, or eggs, and LH stimulates ovulation—release of a mature ovum.

EMPHASIZE. Help students to understand that neither the release of hormones by the endocrine system nor the action of such hormones on the body is under conscious control. This principle applies equally to glands involved with digestion and those involved with sexual maturation.

During puberty, teens experience growth spurts and other physical changes at different ages and different rates. *What triggers these changes during adolescence?*

Secondary Sex Characteristics

During puberty, at each teen's own pace, the reproductive organs mature and begin to release the hormones that cause the development of secondary sex characteristics. In males, testosterone causes the shoulders to broaden and facial, underarm, and pubic hair to grow. The voice deepens and muscles develop. The bones become longer and larger. In females, estrogen and progesterone cause breast development, growth of underarm and pubic hair, and widened hips.

Along with development of the secondary sex characteristics comes increased activity of the oil and sweat glands. This is why acne becomes a problem during adolescence. Increased sweat and underarm hair can also cause body odor. Good hygiene is especially important during this time and will help minimize these problems.

 Good hygiene can help to control acne. Medication may be required in severe cases. *Why do you need to pay more attention to personal hygiene during puberty?*

CRITICAL THINKING. Growth in puberty proceeds in a specific order: feet, then hands, then arms and legs. Have students explain how this growth sequence contributes to possible awkwardness and/or clumsiness during adolescence.

Concerns Over Changes of Puberty

Remember that although adolescents go through all the changes of puberty, each person's time line is different. There is no other time in life when there is such a wide variation in sizes and shapes of people who are the same age. This variation can cause concern for some teens. Growth spurts during puberty depend largely on each person's genetic inheritance and are set in motion by hormones. These hormonal changes cause feelings and sensations never experienced before. It is important to know that everyone grows at a rate that is just right for them.

Lesson 3 *Review*

LESSON 3 REVIEW ANSWERS ARE FOUND ON PAGE TM13.

Reviewing Facts and Vocabulary

1. What is the endocrine system?
2. What role do hormones play during puberty?
3. Name the organs that release hormones that cause the development of secondary sex characteristics.

Thinking Critically

4. **Synthesizing.** Appraise the significance of physical changes that occur during adolescence. How might the development of secondary sex characteristics affect an adolescent's social and emotional development?

5. **Analyzing.** Compare the secondary sex characteristics that develop during puberty for females with those that develop for males.

Applying Health Skills

Managing Stress. A common stressor for teens is to worry over height, weight, or appearance. Make a poster that focuses on how each individual is unique. On the poster, provide a positive tip for handling this stressor, such as thinking positively or being physically active.

Chapter 1 *Review*

CHAPTER 1 REVIEW ANSWERS ARE FOUND ON PAGE TM14.

➤ REVIEWING FACTS AND VOCABULARY

1. Why is it important to have factual information about sexual activity?

2. Give one example of a decision that could affect your total health in a positive way.

3. Identify the six steps in the decision-making process.

4. List the goal-setting steps.

5. Define *empathy*.

6. What gland controls much of the endocrine system? Where is it located?

7. Identify the male and female reproductive organs that produce sex cells. Which hormones does each organ release?

8. Name three secondary sex characteristics that occur in males and three that occur in females.

➤ THINKING CRITICALLY

9. **Synthesizing.** Give a specific example of a decision that could affect your physical, mental/emotional, and social well-being.

10. **Applying.** Select a goal that you worked toward achieving. Compare and contrast the steps you took to the steps in the goal-setting process. Are there any steps in the process that might have helped you attain your goal?

11. **Analyzing.** Choose three of the developmental tasks based on the work of Robert Havighurst. Give an example of an action you can take to succeed in each of them.

12. **Analyzing.** Identify a task that you could not perform when you were a child that you can perform now as a result of cognitive development.

13. **Evaluating.** What might you say to help a friend who is depressed because he is shorter than all of his peers?

14. **Synthesizing.** You've noticed that your friend has facial hair that he did not have last year. You've also noticed that he develops body odor by the end of the school day. What should your friend recognize about the changes that occur during puberty, and what might you tell him?

➤ APPLYING HEALTH SKILLS

15. **Advocacy.** Create a pamphlet about the importance of making healthful decisions that promote individual, family, and community health. Include examples of appropriate and effective decision-making skills. Be sure to use catchy headlines, graphics, and other visuals to engage the reader.

16. **Practicing Healthful Behaviors.** Write a short story that teaches teens the importance of showing responsibility in caring for their physical, mental/emotional, and social health. Describe how their bodies, minds, and emotions are changing and why they will benefit from practicing healthful behaviors.

BEYOND *the* Classroom

Parent Involvement

Community programs. With your parents, contact local programs that provide opportunities for teens to volunteer in the community. Create a reference file listing ways teens can reach out to others while developing their own emotional and social maturity.

School and Community

Endocrine system. Using the Internet or library resources, find out more about the endocrine system. Choose two endocrine glands not discussed in this chapter. Write a paragraph about each gland, listing the hormone each gland produces and the effect of the hormone on the body.

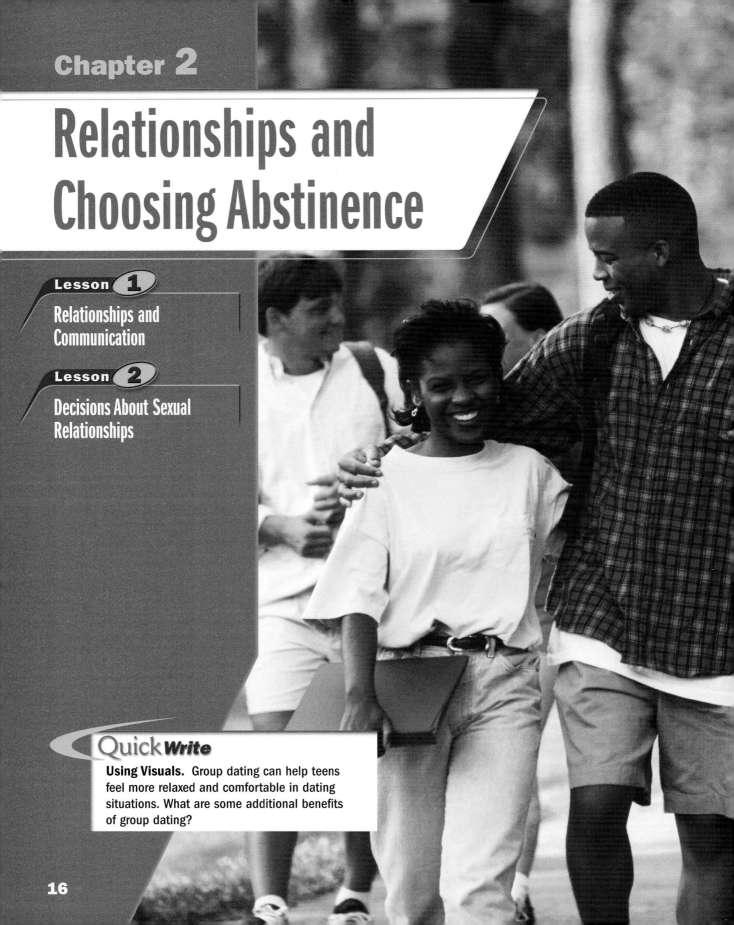

Relationships and Choosing Abstinence

Lesson 1

Relationships and Communication

Lesson 2

Decisions About Sexual Relationships

Quick*Write*

Using Visuals. Group dating can help teens feel more relaxed and comfortable in dating situations. What are some additional benefits of group dating?

Relationships and Communication

VOCABULARY

values
peer pressure
communication
conflict

YOU'LL LEARN TO

- Evaluate the effects of family relationships on physical, mental/emotional, and social health.

- Evaluate the positive and negative effects of relationships with peers.

- Demonstrate communication skills that build and maintain healthy relationships.

QUICK START On a piece of paper, list three qualities of healthy relationships. Then, in a paragraph, explain why those qualities are important and how having healthy relationships can contribute to a fulfilling life.

Humans are social beings. We need other people in our lives. In order to fulfill the basic emotional need to belong, we need to feel that we are valued members of a group. Throughout our lives, we will belong to many different groups.

Family and Friends

The first group that most people belong to is their family. The family is the basic unit of society. Besides ensuring that its members' needs for food, clothing, and shelter are met, the family provides guidance to help children learn to function in society. It is within the family that we first learn to get along with others. Families also teach us our **values**, *the beliefs and standards of conduct that are important to a person.* Values are also instilled through cultural heritage, religious beliefs, and family traditions. You apply your values to the decisions that you make every day.

CRITICAL THINKING. Ask students to identify basic values that they consider important. How do these values influence their decisions and their behavior?

DISCUSS. Review with students the developmental tasks adolescents go through during the teen years. Ask students to discuss the importance of empathy and respect in forming mature peer relationships.

As we mature, our experience with society increases—we meet people outside of our family and we begin to make friends and become a part of other groups. These relationships help us learn about ourselves and others. As we get older, our friendships may change—some may become deeper while others change only slightly. Sometimes, we may outgrow relationships.

Relationships in Adolescent Years

In Chapter 1, you learned about the fundamental tasks of adolescence. Forming more mature relationships with your peers is important for your social health. Many activities during the teen years can broaden and deepen your experience with individuals and groups, helping you to achieve this developmental task. Being involved in a variety of school, religious, and community activities can promote your mental/emotional and social growth.

Peer Pressure

As you develop relationships with individuals and groups, you will probably experience peer pressure. **Peer pressure** is *the influence that people your own age may have on you.* Peer pressure can be positive or negative. For example, members of a school club may encourage each other to develop a special talent. On the other hand, a person who takes risks may try to persuade a friend to participate in high-risk behaviors such as using drugs or engaging in sexual activity.

Peer pressure is especially influential for adolescents with low self-esteem. In order to feel a sense of belonging, they may engage in high-risk behaviors or other activities that go against their values.

Dating

During the teen years, dating is often considered an important social activity. Group dates offer teens opportunities to interact with a variety of people while getting to know someone better in an informal setting. Teens may feel less nervous about a first date when they are in a group.

Dating may lead to steady dating, a situation in which two people date each other exclusively. Steady dating may give a person a sense of security but it may also interfere with developing other healthy relationships. If a relationship doesn't work out, you may think, "Something is wrong with me." This is simply not true. It really means that the other person has preferences or interests that are different from yours. Although rejection is difficult and breaking up can be painful, it is important not to lose your feelings of self-worth because of another person.

Communication

Communication—*the process through which you send messages to and receive messages from others*—is essential to any relationship. Good communication skills will help you keep relationships healthy and form more mature relationships with your peers.

Good Communication Skills

Good communication means clearly expressing your feelings, thoughts, ideas, and expectations. Here are some suggestions for improving your communication skills. Practice them when there is no problem—you will be more likely to use them when a problem arises.

1. Use "I" messages to avoid placing blame.

2. Maintain a polite tone in your voice.

3. Speak directly to the person.

4. Provide a clear, organized message that states the situation.

5. Body language should match your words.

By using "I" messages, you are taking responsibility for how you feel. "You" statements, such as "You are rude when you keep me waiting," send the message that you are blaming someone else. When people are blamed or accused of something, they usually become defensive. This causes conflict. When you use an "I" message, such as "I understood we were meeting at 4:00 and I am unhappy that I had to wait two hours," others have no need to be defensive and are more likely to discuss the issue.

EMPHASIZE. Group dating is a good way to get to know someone.

CRITICAL THINKING. Ask students to explain how good communication is essential in mature relationships.

Effective communicators are able to clearly state the situation. *What are some other skills effective communicators use?*

CRITICAL THINKING. Have students think of ways that good communication skills can help them avoid behaviors in which they do not want to participate.

EMPHASIZE. Stress that conflicts are normal in any kind of relationship. It is important to have a strategy to deal with conflicts before they occur.

When conflicts occur, remember to stay calm and follow the T.A.L.K. strategy. *Why is it important to take time out if the individuals involved in a conflict are feeling emotional or upset?*

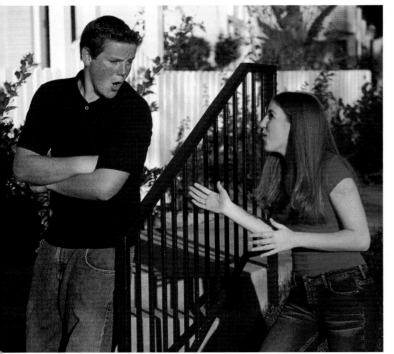

Good Listening Skills

Good communication also means listening to what other people say. Everyone wants to feel that he or she is being heard and is not going to be judged, interrupted, or ignored. Follow these guidelines for being a good listener:

▶ **Give your full attention to the person speaking.** Eliminate distractions, such as a radio or television.

▶ **Focus on the speaker's message.** Look for the central concept that the speaker is trying to convey.

▶ **Indicate your interest.** Lean toward the speaker; nod at or encourage the other person. Maintain eye contact.

▶ **Remember what the speaker has said.** When it's your turn to speak, summarize your understanding of what the other person has said. If you have misunderstood, the speaker can correct you.

▶ **Use positive body language.** A smile and a nod indicate that you are interested and open to communication.

Conflict

Whether relationships are close or merely casual, conflicts are inevitable. **Conflict** is *any disagreement, struggle, or fight.* Some of the most common reasons for conflict include lack of communication between two people and their attempts to meet different needs. When conflicts or disagreements occur, relying on the T.A.L.K. strategy will help both parties reach a peaceful resolution.

1. T—Take time out.

2. A—Allow each person to express his or her opinion uninterrupted.

3. L—Let each person take turns to ask questions and clarify any statements.

4. K—Keep brainstorming to find a good solution.

Compromise, or give-and-take, is essential to every healthy relationship. When both people feel like winners in a conflict, everyone benefits. For example, friends might agree to alternate activities when spending time together so that each person has a chance to choose an activity.

Conflict and Dating

Becoming skilled at "choosing your battles," or deciding when it is worthwhile to take a stand, can help you avoid unnecessary conflict. Determine if the issue is really important, and if it will matter tomorrow, a week from now, or next month. Thoughtful evaluation of the situation will help you decide if there truly is a conflict. Then you can use the T.A.L.K. strategy to resolve a conflict without compromising your values.

In any relationship, people must communicate in order to have their feelings known and understood. Good communication is especially important in a dating relationship. Both people on a date must be willing to express themselves honestly and listen to what the other person is saying. Suppose you are on a date with someone you really like. You've spent time getting to know each other, and you have fun together. What are some expectations you might have of the person you are dating? How would your date know what your expectations are? Conflict can occur when two people's expectations are different and are not clearly communicated. Effective communication will help you maintain healthy, mature relationships.

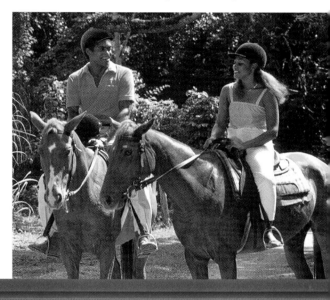

Teens in a dating relationship should identify a variety of activities that they can both enjoy. *What are other strategies for maintaining a healthy dating relationship?*

 Lesson 1 *Review*

LESSON 1 REVIEW ANSWERS ARE FOUND ON PAGE TM16.

Reviewing Facts and Vocabulary

1. Evaluate ways your parents, guardians, and other family members contribute to physical and mental/emotional health and help you establish healthy relationships.

2. Define the term *peer pressure* and evaluate the positive and negative effects of relationships with peers.

3. List three benefits of group dating.

Thinking Critically

4. **Analyzing.** Explain and demonstrate the importance of using good communication skills in building and maintaining healthy relationships. Give two examples.

5. **Synthesizing.** Make a list of positive ways you can develop healthy relationships with your peers. Describe specific actions you can take to become a good friend.

Applying Health Skills

Analyzing Influences. Divide a sheet of paper into two columns. Label the first column *Family* and the second one *Peers*. In each column, list the ways in which that group of people has influenced you in your relationships. Provide at least two specific examples for each column, and evaluate whether the influence on your behavior was positive or negative.

Decisions About Sexual Relationships

VOCABULARY

abstinence
intimacy
refusal skills

YOU'LL LEARN TO

- Analyze the importance and benefits of abstinence from sexual activity in promoting emotional health and preventing pregnancy, STDs, and HIV/AIDS.

- Evaluate ways to practice abstinence in a dating relationship.

- Demonstrate refusal strategies to reinforce the decision to remain abstinent.

QUICK START Describe a decision that a teen in a dating relationship may have to make. Apply the steps of the decision-making process to help the teen make a health-enhancing choice.

▼ **Mature teens effectively communicate their decisions about sexual limits.** *What are some healthful ways for dating teens to demonstrate respect for one another's decisions?*

I n a dating relationship, good communication is critical for setting limits regarding sexual involvement. Each person must make decisions about what he or she wants from the relationship and communicate those decisions effectively. These important decisions are made more complicated by new and sometimes confusing feelings, especially physical attraction to another person. These normal, healthy feelings are caused by hormones, and it is important to recognize that physical attraction is not the same as being in love. Sometimes, it is only infatuation, exaggerated feelings of passion for another person.

Decisions About Sexual Behavior

I t is perfectly normal for young people to decide that they are not ready for a sexual relationship. As a matter of fact, many teens are making the choice to practice abstinence. **Abstinence** is *a deliberate decision to avoid harmful behaviors, including sexual activity before marriage and the use of alcohol, tobacco, and other drugs.*

Your family may already have set limits regarding dating relationships. Remember that seeking advice and feedback from parents or guardians is an important part of the decision-making process as you mature. They can help you determine how to set your own limits that will protect your health and safety.

Abstinence from sexual activity is the healthy, safe choice for teens. It is the only method that is 100 percent effective in preventing unplanned pregnancy, sexually transmitted diseases (STDs) and the sexual transmission of HIV/AIDS. However, some abstinent teens may feel pressured by their peers to become sexually active. Sometimes, peer pressure may lead teens to boast about imaginary sexual experiences in an attempt to impress others.

Messages about sexual behavior come from many different sources—peers, magazines, books, music, television, and movies—and are often confusing and contradictory. How can you decide for yourself about remaining abstinent? Ask yourself the following questions:

► Have I communicated with my boyfriend/girlfriend about my expectations in this relationship?

► Do my boyfriend's/girlfriend's beliefs about premarital sexual activity differ from my own?

► Does my boyfriend/girlfriend pressure me to engage in behaviors that I'm uncomfortable with?

► How would I feel about myself if I engaged in sexual activity?

► Am I prepared to deal with an unplanned pregnancy?

► What would I do if I found out I had an STD?

► How would I handle being infected with HIV, the virus that causes AIDS?

► How would being a teen parent affect my goals and dreams?

People who choose abstinence demonstrate self-respect and maturity. *How will abstinence help you reach your goals?*

CRITICAL THINKING. Have students discuss some of their favorite television shows. Ask them to describe how the shows portray sexual behavior. Have them explain what kind of messages the shows send to teens.

Practicing Abstinence Until Marriage

By carefully considering and honestly answering the questions above, many teens make the healthful decision to practice abstinence until marriage. Abstinence does not mean doing without intimacy or physical contact in a close, special friendship. **Intimacy** is *a closeness between two people that develops over time.* For example, a couple can hold hands, hug, kiss, and grow to know and understand each other while practicing abstinence. When teens choose abstinence, they are demonstrating

Practicing abstinence requires genuine commitment. *How can dating in groups help teens keep a commitment to be abstinent?*

DISCUSS. How can being sexually active interfere with a teen's plans for the future? Remind students of the risks of pregnancy and sexually transmitted diseases.

CHARACTER ✎ CHECK

Respect. When you make the responsible decision to practice abstinence, you are demonstrating respect for your body. **In what other ways does practicing abstinence demonstrate respect for self and others? Summarize your thoughts in a paragraph.**

EMPHASIZE. It is very important for a person practicing abstinence to communicate honestly and clearly with his or her date or girlfriend/boyfriend. To do this, individuals must be clear as to why he or she is choosing abstinence.

maturity and the ability to take responsibility for their health and well-being. They also show respect and care for their dating partners.

Benefits of Abstinence

Young people have identified a variety of reasons to remain abstinent until marriage, including the following benefits to their physical, mental/emotional, and social health:

▶ Abstinence eliminates both persons' risks of contracting a sexually transmitted disease, including HIV/AIDS.

▶ Abstinence is the only 100 percent effective method to avoid unplanned pregnancy.

▶ Becoming sexually active goes against their personal values and those of their family.

▶ Abstinence can allow a couple to build a deeper friendship.

Teens are not physically, mentally, emotionally, or financially ready for the short-term and long-term consequences of engaging in sexual activity. In addition to the effects on physical and mental/emotional health, there are legal consequences. It is illegal for an adult to have sexual contact with anyone under the age of consent, which varies from state to state. In many states it is illegal for unmarried minors to engage in sexual activity. These negative effects can disrupt a teen's life and interfere with his or her plans for the future.

Practicing Your Decision to Be Abstinent

If you have made the decision to abstain from sexual activity, a well thought-out plan of action will help you uphold that choice. The following steps can help you.

▶ Make a detailed list of your reasons for choosing abstinence.

▶ Discuss your feelings, your decision, and your expectations of the relationship with your boyfriend or girlfriend.

▶ Place yourself in situations that reinforce your decision to be abstinent. When dating, for example, choose well-lit places that encourage conversation, or date in groups.

▶ Plan your time together—where you will go, how long you will stay, and what time you will go home.

Using Refusal Skills

As you mature, you will assume more and more responsibility for your actions. This means that you always try to make the best possible decisions for your health, safety, and well-being. Sometimes, however, you may feel pressured to make risky decisions that go against your values. In these situations, you will need to stand up for yourself and firmly say no. Practicing refusal skills will help you uphold your intentions and values. **Refusal skills** are *communication strategies that help you say no effectively.* Follow these tips to strengthen your refusal skills.

▶ Use your decision-making skills as outlined in Chapter 1.

▶ When resisting pressure, simply say no, without feeling that you need to justify yourself. Repeat yourself if necessary.

DISCUSS. Ask students to give examples of situations in which compromise might not be the best solution and to explain why.

Health Skills Activity

Refusal Skills: Communicating Your Pledge of Abstinence

Marla and Dwayne have been dating for several months. Marla is dedicated to remaining abstinent, but she is embarrassed to talk about it with Dwayne.

Marla usually tries to plan dates that include activities they both enjoy doing with groups of their friends. Lately, though, Dwayne has been suggesting that they spend more time alone together.

One day, Dwayne tells Marla that he loves her and says that if she really loved him she would want to add sexual activity to their relationship.

Marla does care for Dwayne, but she is also committed to her pledge of abstinence. What can Marla do to effectively communicate to Dwayne her intention to remain abstinent?

What Would You Do?
Use the following refusal skills to write a dialogue between Marla and Dwayne, in which Marla remains true to her abstinence pledge and effectively communicates her decision to Dwayne.

1. Say no in a firm voice.
2. Repeat yourself if necessary.
3. Use appropriate body language.
4. If possible, suggest an alternative.
5. Leave if necessary.

▶ Be polite but keep your tone firm. Do not insult or yell at the other person, but do use a firm tone of voice and direct eye contact. To help show that you mean what you say, avoid body language that implies you are nervous or unsure.

▶ If possible, suggest an alternative activity that is acceptable to you.

▶ Do not compromise when you feel strongly about something. Compromise can be a passive way of saying yes.

▶ Avoid the use of alcohol and other drugs. The use of these substances impairs your judgment and your ability to make healthy decisions.

▶ If the other person persists and continues to pressure you, *leave*. Go someplace where you feel safe and comfortable.

Whenever you use your refusal skills, congratulate yourself for standing up for what you believe in. You will feel stronger for not compromising your values. Remember, true friends will not challenge you to do something that goes against your values. Develop friendships with people who share your values and interests. They will not push you to do something you don't want to do. They will respect your ability to make the right decision for yourself. You will find it's much easier to resist negative peer pressure from someone else when you have friends who stand by you and support your decision.

▶ Lesson 2 *Review*

LESSON 2 REVIEW ANSWERS ARE FOUND ON PAGE TM17.

Reviewing Facts and Vocabulary

1. Define *abstinence*.

2. Analyze the importance and benefits of abstinence in promoting emotional health and the prevention of pregnancy, STDs, and HIV/AIDS. List four reasons to practice abstinence from sexual activity.

3. Describe and demonstrate with examples three refusal strategies you can take to reinforce a decision to remain abstinent.

Thinking Critically

4. **Evaluating.** What would you say to a friend who says that he or she will make a decision about sexual activity when faced with the problem, not before? Explain your reasoning.

5. **Applying.** Engaging in sexual activity before marriage can have physical, mental/emotional, and legal consequences. Provide two examples of each of these types of consequences.

Applying Health Skills

Practicing Healthful Behaviors. Write a one-act play. Focus on someone using the strategies listed in this lesson to maintain his or her choice to be abstinent in a dating relationship.

CHAPTER 2 REVIEW ANSWERS ARE FOUND ON PAGE TM18.

➤ REVIEWING FACTS AND VOCABULARY

1. What basic social unit serves as the foundation for your values?
2. Define the term *communication*.
3. Why is it important to use "I" messages when discussing an issue or giving an opinion?
4. List four ways that you can practice good listening skills.
5. Describe the issues that a teen might consider when making decisions about remaining abstinent.
6. What is *intimacy*? Explain how a couple can establish intimacy while practicing abstinence.
7. What aspects of a date can you plan in advance, and how might such planning help you avoid high-risk situations?
8. What are *refusal skills*?

➤ THINKING CRITICALLY

9. **Synthesizing.** Values develop from many different sources, including your family, religious beliefs, personal experiences, and cultural heritage. Make a two-column chart. In the left column, list ten values that are important to you. In the right column, identify the people or experiences that helped you to form these values.
10. **Synthesizing.** Explain how peer pressure can have either a positive or a negative effect on a person's decision about whether to remain abstinent.
11. **Evaluating.** What healthful alternatives would you recommend to someone who is thinking about compromising his or her beliefs about sexual activity to avoid conflict with his or her girlfriend or boyfriend?
12. **Analyzing.** Explain why practicing abstinence is a sign of emotional maturity.
13. **Analyzing.** Write a paragraph describing ways that communication skills and refusal skills can help teens maintain a healthy dating relationship.
14. **Synthesizing.** Jackie has agreed to go to the prom with Ryan. She wants to remain abstinent, but she is extremely attracted to Ryan, and she has a feeling that he will pressure her to engage in sexual activity. What advice might you give her?

➤ APPLYING HEALTH SKILLS

15. **Communication Skills.** Create a skit with dialogue in which two teens reach an agreement on where to go on a date. Act out the skit with a partner, using polite tones and body language to match the words in the skit.
16. **Decision Making.** Write a short story that teaches teens the importance of making responsible decisions about sexual relationships. For example, the main character in your story might be faced with a challenge on a date, causing him or her to use the six steps of the decision-making process.
17. **Advocacy.** Create a pamphlet that encourages teens to practice abstinence. Include examples of appropriate and effective communication skills. Be sure to use catchy headlines, graphics, and other visuals to engage the reader.

BEYOND the Classroom

Parent Involvement

Group activities. Research to find out where teens in your community can go on group dates that involve safe and healthy activities. Draw a map of your town or city that shows where these places are located. Share the map with your parents.

School and Community

Thinking of the future. Research the difficulties that teens face when they experience an unplanned pregnancy. Find out how having a baby affects a teen's education, finances, and social life. Report your findings to the class.

The Reproductive System

Quick *Write*

Using Visuals. Many changes occur during the teen years. Hormones control these physical and emotional changes. How can keeping your health triangle in balance help you through the changes of adolescence?

The Male Reproductive System

VOCABULARY

scrotum
testes
testosterone
sperm
epididymis
penis
semen
vas deferens

YOU'LL LEARN TO

- Analyze the relationship between good personal hygiene, health promotion, and disease prevention.

- Describe the functioning of the male reproductive system.

- Relate the importance of early detection and warning signs that prompt individuals to seek health care for the male reproductive system.

QUICK START Fold a sheet of paper into thirds to make a three-column chart. List the external male reproductive organs in column 1. List the internal male reproductive organs in column 2. Note any questions you have about the structure or function of the male reproductive system in column 3.

Male and female reproductive systems produce the cells needed to make a new human being. In this lesson, you will learn structures of the male reproductive system and how they function.

External Male Reproductive Organs

The scrotum, the testes (also called testicles), and the penis are the external male reproductive organs. Each has its own role to play in the structure and function of the male reproductive system.

The Scrotum and the Testes

The **scrotum** is *a loose sac of skin that hangs outside the body.* It holds the **testes**, which are the *male sex glands.* The testes have two main functions: they manufacture **testosterone**, *the male sex hormone,* and they produce **sperm**, the *male reproductive cells.*

To produce sperm, the temperature of the testes must be a few degrees lower than the normal body temperature of 98.6°F.

EMPHASIZE. Help students understand that keeping the temperature of the testes within a fairly narrow range allows normal sperm formation. The distance between the scrotum and the body changes; the skin of the scrotum tightens up to bring the testes closer to the body to increase heat, and loosens to move the testes farther away from the body to reduce heat.

Sperm can only be seen under a microscope. Each sperm consists of a head, a midpiece, and a tail that moves it through the various ducts and out of the body. *Where are sperm produced?*

DISCUSS. The head of a sperm includes enzymes needed to enter the ovum. Have students consider how this process might work and why it may be important.

EMPHASIZE. Point out that semen is a complex mixture of sperm and several secretions that keep sperm alive and active as they make their way out of the body.

The scrotum keeps the testes at the right temperature by holding the testes away from or close to the body, as needed. When body temperature rises, muscles attached to the scrotum relax, causing the testes to lower away from the body. If body temperature lowers, the muscles tighten and the testes move closer to the body for warmth. Tight clothing that holds the testes too close to the body may interfere with sperm production.

Sperm are produced in a section of the testes called the seminiferous tubules. There are about 800 of these threadlike tubes in each testis that produce thousands of sperm every second. Once sperm are produced, they move into the **epididymis**, *a highly coiled structure located on the back side of each testis.* Maturation of the sperm continues in the epididymis and takes about 64 days.

A mature sperm is one of the smallest cells in the body. Each sperm carries 23 chromosomes—half the number present in other body cells. When a sperm unites with a female ovum, which also carries 23 chromosomes, the result is one cell with 46 chromosomes and production of a human offspring.

The Penis

The **penis** is a *tubelike organ that functions in both sexual reproduction and the elimination of body wastes.* When spongelike tissues of the penis fill with blood, the penis becomes enlarged and hard, or erect. Erections are a normal part of being a male, and they occur more easily and more often during puberty.

The penis must be erect for **semen**, *a mixture of sperm and glandular secretions*, to leave the body. The release of semen from the penis is called ejaculation. As many as 300 million to 500 million sperm are released in the average ejaculation. Fertilization—the joining of a male sperm cell and a female egg cell—can result if ejaculation occurs during sexual intercourse. Erection does not mean, however, that semen must be released; the penis can return to its unerect state without ejaculation.

All male babies are born with a fold of skin known as foreskin that covers the end of the penis. Surgical removal of the foreskin is called circumcision. Circumcisions are performed for religious and cultural reasons, but for many years they were also performed because they were thought to be necessary to prevent infection. Doctors now feel circumcision is not medically necessary with good personal hygiene.

Internal Male Reproductive Organs

The internal male reproductive structures play important roles in the male reproductive system. These structures include the vas deferens, the urethra, the seminal vesicles, the prostate gland, and Cowper's glands. These structures are shown in **Figure 3.1** on page 32.

The Vas Deferens and the Urethra

After sperm mature in the epididymis of a testis, they travel into the **vas deferens**, *a long tube that connects each epididymis with the urethra*, which exits the body at the tip of the penis. Lined with smooth muscle that contracts to move sperm through the duct, the vas deferens is the main carrier of sperm. Viable sperm can remain in this duct for several months.

The vas deferens loops over the pubic bone, around the bladder, and through the prostate gland. It is 16 to 18 inches long. As it passes through the prostate gland, it narrows and becomes the ejaculatory duct, which opens into the urethra. As sperm travel through these ducts, they mix with several fluids to form semen.

The urethra is a duct that extends 6 to 8 inches from the urinary bladder, through the prostate, to the tip of the penis. The urethra carries urine from the bladder out of the body; it also carries semen out of the body. Although the urethra carries both urine and semen, it is physically impossible to carry both at the same time. When the penis becomes erect, a ring of muscular tissue closes off the bladder and keeps urine from entering the urethra.

The Reproductive Glands

The purpose of the glands in the reproductive system is to add secretions that support the sperm as they move through the reproductive system. Semen consists of sperm and secretions from the testes, the seminal vesicles, the prostate, and Cowper's glands.

The seminal vesicles contribute the most secretions to semen—about 60 percent of the total volume. There are two of these vesicles, or sacs, located on either side of the prostate gland, each measuring about 2 inches in length. The secretions from the seminal vesicles help make sperm mobile and provide them with nourishment. The secretions from the seminal vesicles empty into the ejaculatory ducts and then travel with the sperm and other testicular secretions that account for about 5 percent of the total volume of semen into the urethra.

Did You Know?

When exposed to cool temperatures—and during sexual arousal—the scrotum contracts and pulls the testes closer to the body where they can absorb heat from the pelvic cavity.

CRITICAL THINKING. A male who does not want to father any children can have a vasectomy. The vas deferens is cut and tied, preventing sperm from leaving the body. The sperm are absorbed into the body. Ask students to explain why this procedure does not prevent semen from being created and exiting the body.

The male reproductive system includes both external and internal organs.

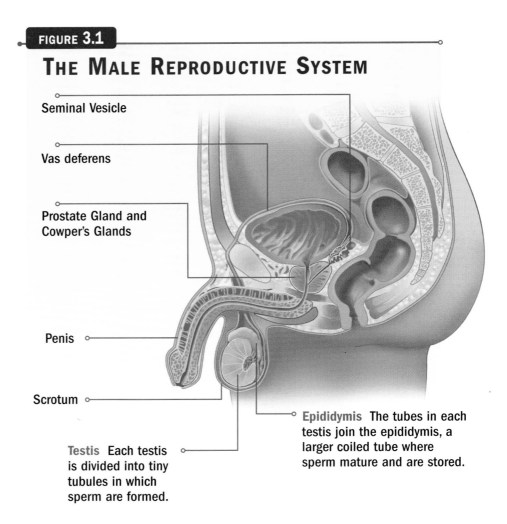

FIGURE 3.1

THE MALE REPRODUCTIVE SYSTEM

Seminal Vesicle

Vas deferens

Prostate Gland and Cowper's Glands

Penis

Scrotum

Epididymis The tubes in each testis join the epididymis, a larger coiled tube where sperm mature and are stored.

Testis Each testis is divided into tiny tubules in which sperm are formed.

CRITICAL THINKING.
Enlargement of the prostate is a common problem for older males. Have students consider possible effects this might have on the ducts that pass through the prostate.

The prostate gland lies just below the bladder and surrounds the urethra. It is about the size of a walnut. This gland secretes a milky, alkaline fluid that mixes with sperm. Acids would destroy the sperm, but this fluid helps neutralize the acids found in the urethra and also those encountered in the female's vagina during intercourse. Just below the prostate gland are two pea-sized glands that open into the urethra. Known as the Cowper's glands, they secrete a clear mucus into the urethra. This secretion is also alkaline and helps carry and protect the sperm by lubricating the urethra and neutralizing the acidity of any urine that might be present.

Concerns About the Male Reproductive System

Nocturnal emissions, hernia, sterility, and cancer of the testes or prostate are some factors males should be aware of in promoting their health.

Nocturnal Emission

In puberty, glands in the male reproductive system begin to produce semen. To relieve the ensuing buildup of pressure, males sometimes have ejaculations while they sleep. These nocturnal emissions may be accompanied by a dream with sexual content. These emissions are also called wet dreams and are perfectly normal.

Hernia Problems

Males are also prone to hernias, which occur when an internal organ pushes through the wall of muscle that normally holds it in. A common hernia in males is the inguinal hernia. Straining abdominal muscles during activities such as heavy lifting can sometimes cause tears that allow part of the intestine to push through the abdominal wall into the scrotum.

Sterility and STDs

Sterility in a male is the inability to produce offspring. The sperm may be weak, deformed, sparse, or nonexistent. Causes of sterility can include overheating of the testes, exposure to certain chemicals, contracting mumps as an adult, and problems with the epididymis, vas deferens, or urethra. Gonorrhea, syphilis, and genital herpes cause infections that can damage the male reproductive system. Complications of an untreated sexually transmitted disease (STD) can result in male sterility.

Testicular Cancer and Problems of the Prostate

Cancer of the testes occurs most often between the ages of 14 and 40 but can affect a male at any age. The main risk factor for testicular cancer is undescended testes. This condition, where one or both testes remain in the abdomen during fetal development, occurs in about 3 percent of boys; surgery can correct the problem. The first sign of testicular cancer is usually a lump or an enlargement of a testis. If testicular cancer is found early, the cure rate is very high. Monthly testicular self-examination is important for early detection.

Another type of cancer among men is prostate cancer. After lung cancer, it is the most common cancer in men. Symptoms include frequent or difficult urination, pain when urinating, blood in the urine, or lingering pain in the back, hips, or pelvis. Prostate cancer in boys and young men is rare, and the above symptoms can also be the result of a urinary infection or an STD.

An enlarged prostate is a common problem among older men. As men age, the prostate may become bigger and block the urethra. This causes difficulty in urinating and can interfere with sexual functioning. Depending on the cause, antibiotics and fluids or surgical procedures are used to treat an enlarged prostate. Males over age 50 should be tested for prostate cancer during routine medical exams.

What is testicular trauma?
It is a painful sensation males experience when the testes are struck, hit, kicked, or crushed, often during sports. Symptoms may include pain, nausea, lightheadedness, dizziness, and sweating. If the pain lasts for more than an hour, or if it is accompanied by extreme swelling or discoloration, males should seek medical treatment immediately.

Males need to wear proper protective gear during sports to protect the reproductive organs from serious injury.

Male Reproductive Health

As the male progresses through puberty and into adulthood, regular medical exams, proper care, and personal hygiene become increasingly important. Regular thorough washing of the external organs is necessary. Uncircumcised males should pull the fold of the foreskin back and wash under it. A substance called smegma, which is made up of dead cells and glandular secretions, can get trapped under the foreskin and cause irritation or infection.

Other care of the external organs includes a monthly self-examination of the testes. This is best done during or after bathing, when the skin of the scrotum is relaxed. The procedure involves gently rolling each testicle between the thumb and fingers. Check for any swelling of the scrotum skin, or lumps on the side of the testicle. If there are any hard lumps or nodules on a testicle or if a change in size, shape, or consistency is noted, professional medical attention is necessary. A lump doesn't necessarily mean cancer is present. Only a doctor can determine if a testicular concern is the result of an infection, a possible cancer, or an unrecognized normal structure such as a blood vessel or duct. All males from puberty on should perform a monthly testicular self-examination.

Lesson 1 Review

LESSON 1 REVIEW ANSWERS ARE FOUND ON PAGE TM20.

Reviewing Facts and Vocabulary

1. Define the terms *scrotum* and *testes* and explain how these parts of the male reproductive system function.

2. List the external and internal male reproductive organs.

3. Analyze the relationship between good personal hygiene, health promotion, and disease prevention. Describe two ways to care for the male reproductive system.

4. Name one male reproductive disorder and relate the importance of early detection and warning signs that prompt individuals to seek treatment to prevent disease.

Thinking Critically

5. **Synthesizing.** Describe the route of sperm from the testes to the penis.

6. **Evaluating.** How might the male reproductive system be affected if the reproductive glands did not function properly?

Applying Health Skills

Accessing Information. Using library resources or the Internet, identify one sexually transmitted disease and determine how it affects the male reproductive system. Research the symptoms, diagnosis, risks, treatment, and prevention of the disease. Write a paragraph discussing why abstinence from sexual activity is the only 100 percent effective method in the prevention of STDs, including HIV/AIDS. Identify your sources, and explain why you believe they are reliable and accurate.

The Female Reproductive System

VOCABULARY

vulva
vagina
cervix
uterus
fallopian tubes
ovaries
ovulation
menstruation

YOU'LL LEARN TO

• Describe the functioning of the female reproductive system.

• Relate the importance of early detection and warning signs that prompt individuals to seek health care for the female reproductive system.

• Analyze the relationship between good personal hygiene and disease prevention.

QUICK START List three facts and three myths you know about the menstrual cycle. Then place a question mark next to each fact you are unsure about or would like to understand better.

The reproductive system is the only system in the body that has different organs for male and female. The female reproductive system functions to produce mature ova, or egg cells. An egg cell, when united with a sperm cell, forms a fertilized ovum that can develop into a new human being.

DISCUSS. Guide students in discussing the benefits of practicing abstinence to promote the health of the reproductive system.

External Female Reproductive Organs

The organs of the female reproductive system are primarily internal. The *external female reproductive organs*, known as the **vulva**, consist of the mons pubis, labia majora, labia minora, vaginal opening, and clitoris.

The Mons Pubis and Labia

The mons pubis is a rounded mound of fatty tissue located in the front of the female body, directly over the pubic bone. The labia majora are the fatty outer folds on either side of the vaginal opening. They make up the outer borders of the vulva. Oil and sweat glands on the inner surface of the labia majora provide moisture and lubrication.

Located between the labia majora are two smaller folds of skin known as the labia minora, which contain oil glands and blood vessels. The labia minora also contain many nerve endings and are highly sensitive. The labia serve as a line of protection against pathogens entering the body and also function in sexual arousal. The combined labia majora and minora surround the vaginal and urethral openings.

The Vaginal Opening

The vaginal opening lies between the labia minora and may be partially blocked by a thin membrane called the hymen. The hymen usually has several openings in it, allowing for the passage of menstrual flow. The membrane may tear during a variety of physical activities. Hymen tissue is flexible and may stay intact during sexual intercourse. However, sperm released at the vaginal opening can enter the vagina through openings in the hymen, which may result in fertilization and pregnancy. Also between the labia minora, just above the vaginal opening, is the urethra, through which urine is secreted.

Below the mons pubis, where the labia minora meet, is a small knob of tissue called the clitoris. The labia minora form a hoodlike covering over the clitoris. The clitoris plays a major role in female sexual arousal and contains many nerve endings and blood vessels, making it highly sensitive. The clitoris becomes engorged, or filled with blood, during sexual arousal.

Internal Female Reproductive Organs

The internal organs of the female reproductive system are the vagina, uterus, fallopian tubes, and ovaries. The organs of the female reproductive system are shown in **Figure 3.2.**

The Vagina and the Uterus

The **vagina** is *an elastic, muscle-lined tube*, 3 to 4 inches long. Also called the birth canal, the vagina is capable of stretching to allow for the birth of a baby. The vagina is the repository for semen when the male ejaculates with the penis inside the vagina during intercourse. It is possible for sperm to enter the reproductive system if the male ejaculates near the vagina. The vagina is also the tube through which menstrual flow exits the female body.

EMPHASIZE. Tell students that the mucous membrane that lines the vagina helps protect delicate vaginal tissues from injury and infection.

Health care professionals, as well as your parents or guardians, are good sources of information. Medical professionals can answer questions about reproductive health.

The vagina leads to the **cervix**, or *neck of the uterus*. The cervical opening is quite small. During childbirth, the cervix dilates, or opens up, to allow passage of the baby. The cervix is also the site of glands that secrete mucus to lubricate the vagina. The **uterus** is *a hollow, muscular organ that receives and holds the fertilized ovum during pregnancy*. The uterus is shaped like an upside-down pear and is also about the size of a pear. Its primary function is to hold and nourish a developing embryo and fetus. During pregnancy the uterus will expand to hold the growing fetus. The uterus has an inner lining called the endometrium, which provides for the attachment of the embryo.

The Fallopian Tubes and the Ovaries

The **fallopian tubes** are *tubes on each side of the uterus that connect the uterus to the region of the ovaries*. They are extremely narrow and are lined with hairlike projections called cilia. Fingerlike projections at the two ends of the tubes surround the top part of the ovaries. Motions of these projections and their cilia gather a released ovum into the tube. If an ovum is present when sperm enter the fallopian tubes, fertilization may occur. Fertilization of the ovum usually occurs in the widest part of the tube, near the ovaries.

The **ovaries** are *the two female sex glands that produce mature ova and female hormones*. They are situated on both sides of the uterus, at the open ends of the tubes. In a mature female, the ovaries release ova on a regular basis and produce the hormones that regulate the female reproductive cycle.

At birth, a female usually has hundreds of thousands of immature ova in her ovaries. As she enters puberty, hormones cause the ova to mature; a few hundred will mature during the reproductive years. *The process of releasing one mature ovum each month into a fallopian tube* is called **ovulation.** The ovum can live about a day in the fallopian tube. If sperm are present during this period, and one successfully penetrates the ovum, fertilization has occurred. Pregnancy begins at this point.

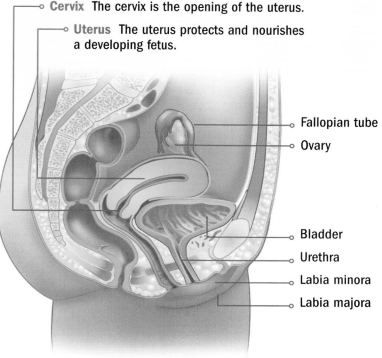

FIGURE 3.2

THE FEMALE REPRODUCTIVE SYSTEM

Cervix The cervix is the opening of the uterus.

Uterus The uterus protects and nourishes a developing fetus.

Fallopian tube
Ovary

Bladder
Urethra
Labia minora
Labia majora

The female reproductive system provides a place for a fertilized ovum to grow.

DISCUSS. During ovulation, usually one egg is released. Fraternal twins occur when two eggs are released during ovulation and both are fertilized. Ask students how identical twins occur.

EMPHASIZE. The hundreds of thousands of immature ova in a female infant's ovaries are only potential sex cells. Only a few hundred cells mature and are released from the ovaries. The rest of the ova degenerate, many of them before they develop into mature ova.

FIGURE **3.3**

THE MENSTRUAL CYCLE

Days 1–13	Day 14	Days 15–20	Days 21–28
A new egg is maturing inside the ovary.	The mature egg is released into one of the fallopian tubes.	The egg travels through the fallopian tube to the uterus.	After seven days, if the egg is not fertilized, menstruation begins.

 The menstrual period occurs when an ovum is not fertilized and the lining of the uterus is shed.

The Menstrual Cycle

Each month, the uterus prepares for a possible pregnancy. Hormones cause the uterine lining, or endometrium, to build up a thick layer of blood vessels and other tissues. This thick layer will support and nourish an embryo if pregnancy occurs. **Figure 3.3** illustrates the menstrual cycle.

Menstruation

If pregnancy does not occur, this lining is not needed and begins to break down. The uterus contracts and the lining is shed through the vaginal opening. *The process of shedding the uterine lining* is called **menstruation**. The blood passing out of the body during menstruation amounts to about three to ten tablespoons. This is blood the body does not need; shedding it does not make a person weak or ill. Because the uterus contracts as the lining is shed, the female may experience abdominal cramps early in the menstrual period.

After the menstrual period ends, usually within 4 to 7 days, the cycle begins again. Hormones signal an ovary to release another ovum around day 14 of the cycle. The uterine lining builds up again, and if pregnancy does not occur, another menstrual period begins around day 28.

Most females begin menstruating between the ages of 10 and 15. A healthy female (who is not pregnant) will continue to menstruate fairly regularly until about age 50 when menopause occurs and menstruation ceases.

Did You Know ?

The ovaries make estrogen and progesterone, the hormones that are primarily responsible for the changes females experience during puberty. Before puberty, estrogen and progesterone are secreted in very small amounts.

Menstrual Health Care

Good hygiene is especially important for females during the menstrual period. There is no odor to the menstrual flow itself, until it mixes with air. Daily bathing or showering is very important, especially during the menstrual period. If a female uses sanitary pads or panty shields to absorb the menstrual flow, she should change them every few hours. If she uses tampons—cylinders of absorbent material that are placed in the vagina—they must be changed frequently and should not be worn overnight. Tampons left in for more than four hours increase the risk of infection.

Concerns About the Female Reproductive System

Although most females enjoy a healthy reproductive system, it is important for a female to be familiar with her body and know what common problems might occur.

Menstrual Problems

Some women experience premenstrual syndrome (PMS) in the week or two before their period. There are a wide range of symptoms, including anxiety, depression, irritability, bloating, mood swings, and fatigue. Some females never experience PMS, but in women who do, it seems to occur most commonly in their thirties. While experts don't agree on the causes of PMS, the symptoms can often be relieved by changes in diet and increasing physical activity. Severe cases may be treated by a physician or nurse practitioner with prescribed medications.

Some females suffer from dysmenorrhea, or severe menstrual cramps. Menstrual cramps are usually mild to moderate and only last several hours. In some females the pain may last a day or two. This pain can be controlled with over-the-counter pain medications. Light exercise can also be helpful, as can a heating pad placed on the abdomen or a warm bath. In cases of severe cramping that does not respond to the above actions, consultation with a medical professional is advised and prescription medication may be necessary.

Amenorrhea is the term for lack of menstruation by age 16 or the stopping of menstruation in a female who previously menstruated. Amenorrhea can be the result of physical defects in the reproductive organs, diseases such as diabetes, tumors, infections, anorexia, or lack of maturation of the endocrine system. Some otherwise healthy females experience amenorrhea from exercising too rigorously. An abnormally low amount of body fat accompanied by excessive exercise, sometimes experienced by professional athletes,

Health Minute

Strategies for Coping with PMS

If you have PMS, your symptoms might include:

► bloating
► backaches
► sore breasts
► depression
► irritability
► difficulty handling stress

To help ease the symptoms of PMS:

► Eat a balanced diet. Avoid foods high in fat, salt, and sugar. Increase the amount of fresh fruits and vegetables in your diet.
► Limit your caffeine intake.
► Participate in regular physical activity.
► Consult your doctor or nurse practitioner if any of these symptoms become severe.

CRITICAL THINKING. Tell students that some tampons have a deodorant chemical in them. This chemical can irritate the lining of the vagina in some females. Ask students to consider whether such chemicals are necessary.

CRITICAL THINKING. Toxic shock syndrome is a condition that can cause serious illness requiring hospitalization. Have students explain how females can reduce their chances of becoming victims of toxic shock syndrome.

can alter hormone levels to a point where ovulation does not occur. A female with amenorrhea should seek professional help to find the cause and correct the problem.

Female Infertility and STDs

Female infertility, the inability to bear children, has a variety of possible causes. The physical blocking of one or both fallopian tubes, for example, prevents ova from passing into the uterus. In other cases, the female does not ovulate, usually because of a hormonal problem. A third cause of female infertility is endometriosis, a condition in which endometrial (uterine lining) tissue grows outside the uterus in other areas of the pelvic cavity. STDs that are left untreated can also lead to infertility. Untreated gonorrhea and chlamydia are the most common STDs that cause infertility in females. Human papillomavirus (HPV) can cause cancer in females.

Problems with Infection

Toxic shock syndrome (TSS) is a rare disease caused by the bacterium *Staphylococcus aureus*. Under certain conditions, the bacterium can produce a toxin that affects the immune system and the liver. Symptoms include sudden onset of fever, chills, vomiting, diarrhea, and a rash. It is believed that using superabsorbent tampons may create an environment in the vagina that allows production of the toxin. High-absorbency tampons should be changed frequently and used with care.

A variety of vaginal infections cause vaginitis, or inflammation of vaginal tissue with discharge, burning, and itching. Yeast infections are caused by a fungus and are generally characterized by a thick, white, odorless discharge accompanied by itching, burning, and painful urination. Yeast infections are rather common and should be diagnosed by a health care professional. Infections may be treated with over-the-counter medications after a definitive diagnosis.

Bacterial vaginosis is the most common type of vaginitis that occurs during the reproductive years. The primary symptom is an odorous vaginal discharge. Trichomoniasis is a vaginal infection that is caused by a protozoan. Symptoms may include odorous discharge, genital itching, and painful urination. A doctor should be consulted if any of these symptoms occur, so that the organism can be identified and the infection treated.

Cancer

In American females, breast cancer is the most common form of cancer and the second leading cause of death after lung cancer. Two-thirds of cases occur in females older than age 50, but breast cancer can occur in younger females. While it is relatively rare, men also get breast cancer. There is no known way to prevent breast cancer; early detection through regular medical exams and monthly self-examinations are the best defenses. Chances of surviving breast cancer are much greater when the cancer is found early. Symptoms include a change in breast or nipple appearance, a lump or swelling in the breast, or a lump in the armpit.

EMPHASIZE. Up to 60 percent of females experience changes in breast tissue called fibrocystic condition, in which small cysts or lumps are present in the breasts. Although fibrocystic condition is not cancerous, any female who finds a breast lump should have an examination by a doctor.

Real-Life Application

Breast Cancer Statistics

The Internet is an excellent source of information about diseases such as breast cancer, as long as you use reliable sites. How can you tell the site shown below is reliable?

NATIONAL CANCER INSTITUTE

Cancer Facts

CIS Home
Cancer.gov
Dictionary
Search

Lifetime Probability of Breast Cancer in American Women

A National Cancer Institute (NCI) report estimates that about 1 in 8 women in the United States (approximately 13.3 percent) will develop breast **cancer** during her lifetime. This estimate is based on cancer rates from 1997 through 1999 as reported in NCI's Surveillance, **Epidemiology**, and End Results (SEER) Program publication *SEER Cancer Statistics Review 1973-1999.*

The 1 in 8 figure means that, if current rates stay constant, a female born today has a 1 in 8 chance of being diagnosed with breast cancer sometime during her life. On the other hand, she has a 7 in 8 chance of never developing breast cancer. A woman's chance of being diagnosed with breast cancer is

from age 30 to age 40	.1 out of 252
from age 40 to age 50	.1 out of 68
from age 50 to age 60	.1 out of 35
from age 60 to age 70	.1 out of 27
Ever	.1 out of 8

In the United States, a female's risk of developing breast cancer sometime during her life is calculated to be 1 in 8. For each of the four decades represented, express the risk as a percentage. Graph your results and describe the trend.

Links to Other Sites
A reputable Web site will provide links so you can learn more about the topic.

Reliable Information
- The most reliable health information is found on sites sponsored by the government, reputable schools and universities, or nonprofit organizations.
- The National Cancer Institute is a government-supported organization that provides the latest scientific research about cancer.
- Commercial sites, such as those maintained by pharmaceutical companies, might have accurate information, but be alert to bias in their reporting.

Reputable Sources
A reputable site will use information from respected journals and from experts in the field.

Another common cancer in females is cervical cancer. Cervical cancer can be detected by getting a Pap test, which detects abnormal cells. A doctor uses a long cotton swab to gather cells from the cervix, and a laboratory checks the cells for abnormalities. If not caught early, cancer cells can spread to surrounding areas, making the cancer much more difficult to treat. There are no early symptoms of cervical cancer, but there are several risk factors: being between the ages of 20 and 30, not having regular Pap tests, having sexual intercourse at an early age, and having multiple sexual partners. All females should have a Pap test every year from age 18 on, or earlier if they are sexually active.

More than 23,000 American females are diagnosed with ovarian cancer each year. Almost 14,000 die from this cancer annually. The symptoms of ovarian cancer are similar to symptoms for other diseases, making it difficult to detect. They include abdominal pressure, bloating, or discomfort; nausea, indigestion, or gas; urinary frequency, constipation, or diarrhea. Ovarian cancer causes abnormal bleeding, unusual fatigue, unexplained weight gain or loss, and shortness of breath. Early detection is critical because only 25 percent of females survive beyond five years if the cancer is diagnosed in advanced stages.

Getting regular physical activity and good nutrition, along with regular medical checkups, are ways to keep the reproductive system healthy.

Female Reproductive Health

In a mature female, the cells in the lining of the vagina are constantly being shed. This often causes a slight vaginal discharge. Bathing regularly, including washing the external female reproductive organs, is an important part of good hygiene. Douches and feminine hygiene sprays are not necessary and may be irritating. Change pads or tampons often. Good personal hygiene and regular professional and self-examinations are important.

The Pelvic Examination

The American Cancer Society recommends yearly pelvic examinations for females by age 18, or earlier if they are sexually active. Before a pelvic exam, the physician and patient often discuss the patient's general health. Then, routine checking of blood pressure, heart rate, and the lungs may be done. Urine and blood samples are also usually taken.

During the actual examination, the breasts and abdomen are checked for lumps. The physician checks the external genitalia for general structure and tissue health, and then performs an exam of the vagina. To help hold the walls of the vagina apart, an instrument called a speculum is inserted into the vagina. This should be a painless procedure, but because the vaginal muscles are strong, being tense may cause some discomfort. With the speculum in place, the physician collects cells from the cervix for a Pap test. This usually completes the examination.

The Breast Self-Examination

Females should perform a breast self-exam (BSE) every month. The best time is right after the menstrual period, when breasts are not tender or swollen. After age 40, an annual mammogram—a series of X rays of the breasts—is recommended in addition to the BSE. See the illustration for steps to perform a breast self-exam.

While taking a shower or bath, gently explore both breast and underarm areas with fingertips. Check the upper and outer parts of each breast, toward the armpit.

Standing in front of a mirror, check for changes in size, shape, and contour of each breast. Check for changes in the nipple, redness, or swelling.

Lie with one arm tucked behind the head. With the other hand, examine the opposite breast for lumps, thickening, or other changes. Move around the breast in a circle, then up and down, going over the entire breast area. Repeat on the other side.

▶ Lesson 2 *Review*

LESSON 2 REVIEW ANSWERS ARE FOUND ON PAGE TM22.

Reviewing Facts and Vocabulary

1. Define the terms *cervix* and *uterus* and explain how these parts of the female reproductive system function.

2. List the external and internal female reproductive organs.

3. Name two disorders of the female reproductive system and relate methods of early detection and warning signs that prompt females to seek health care.

4. Analyze the importance of good personal hygiene for disease prevention. Describe three ways to care for the female reproductive system.

Thinking Critically

5. **Synthesizing.** How might you respond if a friend told you she always experiences PMS the week before her menstrual period?

6. **Analyzing.** A female who is experiencing symptoms of vaginitis goes to see her doctor. Write a paragraph that suggests how the doctor might be able to distinguish among these possible conditions: a yeast infection, bacterial vaginosis, and trichomoniasis.

Applying Health Skills

Advocacy. A favorite cousin of yours who is 22 years old tells you she has never had a Pap test. She says that seeing a doctor and getting a Pap test really isn't important until females are much older. Write your cousin a letter in which you explain what you have learned about regular health care for the female reproductive system.

Hormones and Sexual Feelings

VOCABULARY
hormones

YOU'LL LEARN TO

• Examine the effect of hormones on body systems.

• Demonstrate healthful decision-making skills that show responsible behaviors for your health and the health of others.

 QUICK START On a piece of paper, list as many physical changes or reactions as you can think of that are caused by hormones.

S exual feelings are normal and healthy, and they are controlled by the same hormones that affect your physical growth. **Hormones** are *chemical substances that regulate the activities of different body cells and organs.* Biologically speaking, sexual feelings are essential for the reproductive process.

Sexual Feelings and Response

EMPHASIZE. Both males and females can stop at any point during the first two phases of the sexual response cycle.

S ex hormones cause the body to respond to sexual stimulation, which may result from a kiss, watching a movie scene, holding hands, or thinking about a date. The heart rate increases, breathing speeds up, hands feel clammy, and the face gets flushed. In the male, the penis becomes erect; in the female, vaginal fluids are secreted. These are the body's first responses to excitement. They are entirely natural, and people cannot keep them from occurring. However, a person can and must decide what to do about them. These feelings do not have to be acted upon, and most of the time the responses stop here.

It can become difficult to make a responsible decision once sexual tension builds up, and teens, in particular, can feel overwhelmed by these feelings. It is a good idea to establish predetermined limits on sexual behavior and stop things before they get going. Establishing limits will help you act maturely and responsibly.

Sexual Feelings and Responsible Decisions

Strong physical feelings of attraction to someone should not be confused with love. Remember that hormones cause sexual feelings and that sexual feelings are a normal physical response. You have complete control over what you do about these feelings. When they occur, the important thing is to consciously choose to act responsibly. If you feel overwhelmed by sexual feelings, remind yourself of your long-term goals. Consequences of engaging in sexual behavior may keep you from pursuing your dreams of going to college and having a career. Keeping your goals in mind will help you make mature, responsible decisions.

Goal Setting: Achieving Individual Goals

Ray and Shauna have been dating each other for over a year. They are concerned about what will happen to them in the future.

"Do you think we'll go to the same college?" Ray asks.

"I don't know," Shauna answers. "I really want to study music. You want a career in medical research. I don't think the same school will be right for both of us."

"Well, you could be right, Shauna. But maybe we can find what we want and still be close to each other."

Shauna looks down at her hands and then looks up at her boyfriend. "Oh, Ray. I want to be close to you, too. Do you really think we could both find good programs in schools that are close so we could still spend time together?"

Ray looks back at Shauna. "We won't know unless we try."

What Would You Do?

Apply the steps of the goal-setting process to Ray and Shauna's situation.

1. Identify a specific goal, and write it down.
2. List the steps you will take to reach that goal.
3. Get help and support from others.
4. Set up checkpoints to evaluate progress.
5. Plan a reward for achieving the goal.

If you know what sexual feelings are and understand the body's physical response to those feelings, you can make more responsible decisions concerning them. Remember that your body has some urges that you cannot control. Whether you want to or not, you will sometimes feel hungry, sleepy, or become sexually aroused. Just as you can control when you want to eat and sleep, you also control how you respond to sexual feelings. In controlling how you react to sexual responses, you are taking steps toward maturity and making responsible decisions that will help you to reach your goals for the future and feel good about yourself.

> Responsible decisions about sexual feelings are easier to make when shared activities take place where there are lots of other people and interesting things to see and do.

Lesson 3 *Review*

LESSON 3 REVIEW ANSWERS ARE FOUND ON PAGE TM24.

Reviewing Facts and Vocabulary

1. What causes the body's response to sexual stimulation?
2. Name four of the body's first physiological responses to sexual stimulation.
3. Explain why it is important for a teen to establish predetermined limits on sexual behavior before he or she encounters a situation where a decision must be made.

Thinking Critically

4. **Evaluating.** Are sexual feelings and love the same thing? Explain your answer.

5. **Analyzing.** Discuss how keeping your long-term goals in mind can help you make mature, responsible decisions when you experience sexual feelings. How can these decisions affect your health and the health of others?

Applying Health Skills

Goal Setting. Identify one of your long-term goals. Draw a cartoon strip in which your focus on this goal helps you choose to share with a date an activity that you can enjoy together without finding yourself in a sexual situation.

CHAPTER 3 REVIEW ANSWERS ARE FOUND ON PAGE TM24.

➤ REVIEWING FACTS AND VOCABULARY

1. Describe the structure and function of the epididymis.

2. What is the duct that travels through the penis?

3. Describe the composition of semen.

4. What type of movement can cause an inguinal hernia?

5. What are the fallopian tubes, and what role do they play in the female reproductive system?

6. At what age do most females begin menstruating?

7. Name three causes of sterility in males. Name three causes of infertility in females.

8. What are three symptoms of breast cancer?

➤ THINKING CRITICALLY

9. **Evaluating.** What are some important health decisions you can make to keep your reproductive system healthy?

10. **Synthesizing.** In the reproductive process, how many chromosomes are combined to produce a human offspring? Explain your answer.

11. **Synthesizing.** What is unique about the male and female reproductive systems when compared to the other systems of the body?

12. **Analyzing.** How are ovulation, menstruation, and fertilization interrelated?

➤ APPLYING HEALTH SKILLS

13. **Advocacy.** Your friend has told you in confidence that she has had an unusual vaginal discharge for several days. She is worried and afraid to tell anyone else. Write a dialogue that helps her to overcome her fears and understand how important it is to get medical care so that her condition can be properly identified and treated.

14. **Communication Skills.** A younger sibling of your own gender seems upset. When you ask him or her what is wrong, he or she expresses worry about becoming a teen. Discuss with your younger sibling what to expect when he or she goes through puberty.

BEYOND the Classroom

Parent Involvement

School nurse. Invite the school nurse to the classroom to discuss issues with which teens are often faced concerning puberty and reproductive health. Have parents attend the class session to hear the nurse's presentation. List positive ways that teens can promote their reproductive health.

School and Community

Adolescent health. Interview a health care provider who specializes in adolescent care. Describe the academic preparation necessary for that career and the personal characteristics that would be necessary to be successful in that field.

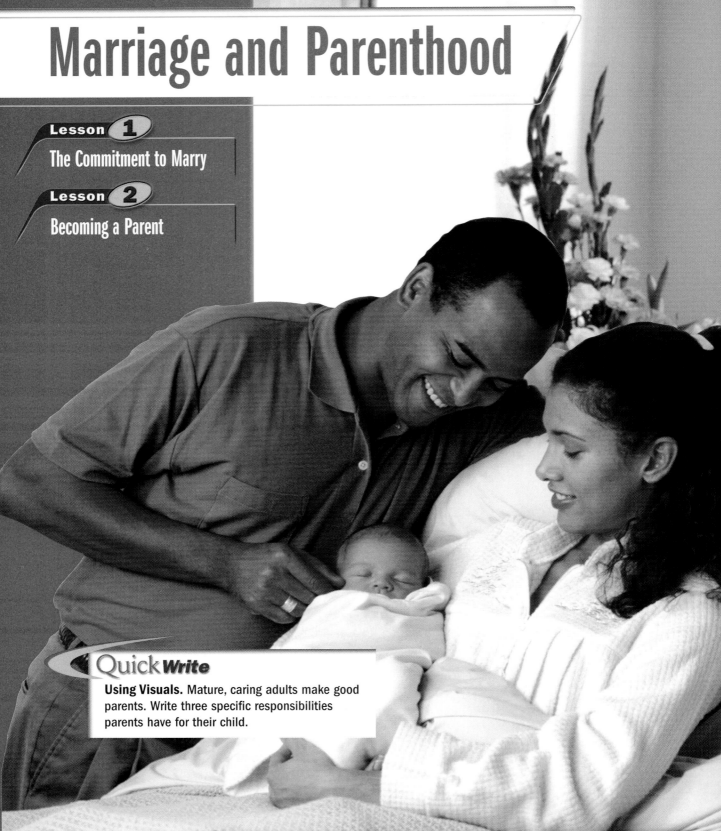

Chapter 4
Marriage and Parenthood

Quick Write

Using Visuals. Mature, caring adults make good parents. Write three specific responsibilities parents have for their child.

The Commitment to Marry

VOCABULARY

commitment
blended family

YOU'LL LEARN TO

• Analyze behavior in a dating relationship that will enhance the dignity, respect, and responsibility relating to marriage.

• Distinguish between a dating relationship and a marriage.

• Demonstrate how couples use effective communication skills in building and maintaining healthy relationships.

• Describe the effects of divorce on adults and children.

• Explain why teens should delay marriage until they are mature adults.

QUICK START Imagine that your boyfriend or girlfriend has proposed marriage to you. Write a letter to him or her explaining why you are not ready for marriage.

Most people expect to marry during their lifetime. Practicing healthful behaviors in dating relationships will help individuals prepare for the dignity, respect, and responsibility of marriage. A marriage is different from a dating relationship in many ways. People who enter a marriage make a lifelong commitment to someone they love. A **commitment** is *a promise or a pledge*. In order for a marriage to be successful, both partners must be ready for new responsibilities and challenges. It is very important that couples honestly evaluate themselves and their relationships in order to determine whether they are ready for the commitment of marriage.

Marriage—A Lifelong Commitment

The most common reason people give for getting married is to enter a lasting relationship with the person they love. Marriage allows couples to share their lives together in an intimate, mature way. It provides companionship in both good and hard times, in adulthood and into later life.

▼ **Marriage is a life-changing commitment that requires maturity from both partners.** *What can couples do to help their chances for a successful marriage?*

People can marry for reasons other than the intention of committing to a future with someone they love. It is important for both members of a couple to closely examine their reasons for marrying and to discuss any doubts they may have about their commitment to one another. They will have a better chance at a successful marriage if they seriously consider how well they know one another and if they discuss their goals and expectations for their life together.

Adjusting to Marriage

Making a commitment to someone is just the beginning of a successful marriage. Couples can become caught up in the excitement of planning a wedding, choosing a place to live together, and sharing their plans with friends and family. In the early stages of the marriage, couples must face the adjustments that come with marriage—sharing living quarters, finances, and families, for example. During this adjustment period, the emotional and social maturity of both partners is crucial to the success of a marriage.

Mature people understand their own needs as well as their spouse's, and they know how to meet those needs in healthy ways. They are willing to compromise and make sacrifices in order to make their marriage successful. Mature couples understand that they will face difficulties in life and that they will work through these difficulties together. Conflicts between a husband and wife will arise, and they will face these challenges with good communication and compassion.

Sociologists have identified a number of factors that are associated with a successful marriage. Generally, the husband and wife

▶ agree on important issues in their relationship.

▶ share common interests and values.

▶ demonstrate affection and share confidences.

▶ show a willingness to compromise and put others first.

▶ share similarities in family backgrounds.

▶ have parents who had a successful marriage.

▶ do not have major conflicts with their in-laws.

▶ have several good friends of both genders.

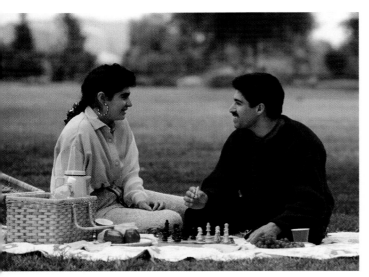

When marriage partners share common interests and activities, their marriage becomes stronger. *Think of a married couple you know and ask how they enjoy their time together.*

▶ had a long period of close association prior to marriage.

▶ have stable jobs and career goals.

▶ agree on how they feel about raising children.

These factors do not guarantee a successful marriage, but partners with many of these characteristics have an increased chance of sharing a lasting, happy marriage.

CRITICAL THINKING. Ask students: Why is it important to understand your own needs? How can understanding one's needs contribute to the success of a marriage?

Health Skills Activity

Communication: Expressing Your Feelings to Your Spouse

Tom and Alicia have been married for four months. Tom wants a night out to go bowling with some friends, but Alicia wants him to stay home with her.

"You're going out again?" Alicia asks, feeling hurt. "We've been so busy lately that we've hardly had time to talk. I was hoping we could go out to dinner and then have a quiet evening at home."

"I promised the guys that I'd be there," Tom says. "We haven't gone bowling in ages."

"You just saw them last weekend at the barbecue," Alicia complains.

"You just don't understand," Tom replies, annoyance creeping into his voice.

"Our marriage should be more important than bowling night!" Alicia cries, storming out of the room.

Tom takes a deep breath and wonders what he should do.

What Would You Do?
Use the communication skills you have learned to write an ending to this scenario in which both spouses express their feelings in productive, non-hurtful ways to resolve their conflict. Be prepared to role-play your response for the class.

1. Use "I" messages.
2. Keep your tone respectful.
3. Provide a clear, organized message that states the problem.
4. Listen to the other person's side without interrupting.

EMPHASIZE. Remind students that when a couple divorces, it does not change the love that the parents have for their children. Children whose parents have divorced need to know that it is okay to love both parents and that it's normal to feel sad, angry, and/or depressed. Talking about their feelings helps young people adjust to the changes in their lives and to accept that their parents' marriage is over.

Seeking help from a professional counselor can help families resolve difficult problems. Even if divorce occurs, counseling can help all family members adjust to the change.

Marriage and Divorce

Divorce has risen dramatically over the past several decades. Overall, nearly 50 percent of marriages end in divorce.

Children can be devastated when parents divorce. The family physically separates, and one parent moves out of the home—sometimes to a distant location. Children may feel sad about not growing up with both parents. Sometimes, children may have to move, which can mean changing schools and leaving old friends behind. Families may have to adjust to a lower standard of living because income is split between two homes. Divorce puts a strain on the entire family and may also impact relationships among individual family members.

In cases where spousal or child abuse is involved, divorce can be a necessary, positive change. It is critical that victims of abuse leave the unsafe environment. Even in situations where there is no abuse, emotional turmoil in the household may create an unhealthy atmosphere for family members. This type of environment can have a permanent negative effect on a child's ability to form healthy relationships later in life. In such cases, divorce may be an appropriate step so that family members can build a new, healthier life.

Although divorce is an adult problem, children may blame themselves for what went wrong and not understand that the divorce had nothing to do with their own behaviors. Because divorce affects children so strongly, it is essential that parents explore all options, including couples counseling, before making the decision to end the marriage. Above all, both partners should remain responsible parents.

Joint Custody

Sometimes divorced couples have joint custody of their children, meaning that the children alternate living with each parent. Depending on work and other schedules, one parent may have the children during the week and the other on weekends, or children may live with one parent for six months of the year and then with the other for the rest of the year. While it can be challenging for children to be shifted back and forth, it is important for both parents to remain involved in their children's lives.

Blended Families

People who get divorced will often choose to remarry, and it is common for the new spouse to have children that he or she brings to the marriage. This creates a **blended family**, or *a family where two adults marry and have children from a previous marriage living with them*. The new couple may also have children together.

Children may experience stress as they adjust to new relationships in the blended family. They may feel resentful of their stepparent or jealous of new stepsiblings. If the stepparent and other children have moved into the child's home, he or she may resent having to share it with others. The child may also struggle to get his or her parent's attention. Emotions such as anger, jealousy, and sadness are normal. To help them adjust to changes after a remarriage, children can talk to their parents, relatives, teachers, counselors, or other trusted adults.

 Joint custody may be challenging, but it allows both parents to remain involved in their children's lives. *What healthful behaviors can help family members adjust to a divorce?*

CRITICAL THINKING. Have students suggest strategies for getting to know new stepparents and stepsiblings.

DISCUSS. Ask students to list what they would like to accomplish in their lives and how marrying in their teens might affect their ability to achieve these goals.

Teen Marriage—A Risky Situation

Since a successful marriage requires both people to be responsible and mature, the odds are not in favor of people who marry in their teens. In fact, approximately 60 percent of teen marriages will end in divorce, many of them within the first few years.

There are good reasons for teens to delay marriage until they are more mature.

▶ Married teens have to focus too soon on another's needs and may not have the time or energy to work on their own personal growth and development.

▶ Married teens may have to postpone college, job training, or beginning a career. When these factors limit their earning power, financial difficulties can seriously threaten the marriage.

▶ If the teen couple married because of a pregnancy, the emotional and financial stresses on the relationship are even more severe.

Lesson 1 *Review*

LESSON 1 REVIEW ANSWERS ARE FOUND ON PAGE TM27.

Reviewing Facts and Vocabulary

1. Define the term *commitment*. How is commitment to a marriage different from commitment to a dating relationship?

2. Explain how a mature couple handles conflicts. How does this demonstrate the use of communication skills in building and maintaining healthy relationships?

3. What is a *blended family*?

4. How does making the decision to delay marriage until they are more mature help teens to promote individual and family health?

Thinking Critically

5. **Analyzing.** Describe some characteristics that indicate a couple is ready for marriage. Explain how these characteristics will enhance the dignity, respect, and responsibility required in a healthy marriage.

6. **Synthesizing.** Make a list of the negative effects of divorce on the children. Explain how family members can deal with a divorce in healthful ways.

Applying Health Skills

Analyzing Influences. Briefly describe a family sitcom or drama on television. Does the show portray relationships between married couples and their children realistically? How do you think media representations of marriage and family relationships influence viewers?

Becoming a Parent

VOCABULARY

heredity
parenting
single-parent
  family

YOU'LL LEARN TO

- Identify reasons why people have children.

- Describe the roles and responsibilities of parents in promoting healthy families.

- Evaluate the effects of family relationships on physical, mental/emotional, and social health.

- Analyze the importance and benefits of abstinence.

 QUICK START Make a word web to describe what you know about caring for an infant. Write "infant" in the middle of a sheet of paper, and then write what responsibilities come to mind. Connect these words and phrases to the center with radiating lines.

Raising children can be the most rewarding and enriching aspect of marriage. Couples who face the many challenges of parenting feel great joy and love as they watch their children develop. Many married couples find that building a healthy, happy family together is an important, fulfilling life experience.

Why People Have Children

People give all kinds of reasons for having children, including passing on the family name and **heredity** (*genetic characteristics passed from parent to child*), giving one's parents a grandchild, wanting to be loved by someone, giving in to pressure from friends or parents, and bringing stability to a shaky marriage. The only truly good reason to bring a child into the world is a readiness to raise a family and share the love of the marriage. A new life is a great responsibility, and love for that new life is essential.

 Parenting involves nurturing a child's physical, mental/emotional, and social development from infancy through adulthood. *List three specific examples of responsibilities parents have toward their children.*

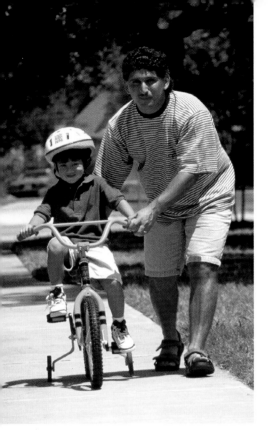

One of the best ways parents can provide a nurturing environment for their children is to spend time with them.

EMPHASIZE. It is important that teens understand that parents make many adjustments to their lives when they have a child. Ask students to think about what sort of changes new parents make.

CRITICAL THINKING. Ask students to think about what parents do to give their children a safe, supportive environment. Ask them why it might be difficult for teen parents to do the same for a child.

Parental Responsibilities

Parenting, *providing care, support, and love in a way that leads to a child's total development,* is one of the most important jobs anyone can have. Parents must provide the basic physical needs of the child—food, clothing, shelter, and medical care. The parents must also meet their child's developmental and emotional needs, ensuring that the child is loved unconditionally and receives the proper nurturing and education to prosper later in life.

Parents also need to give guidance to their children, to help them understand right from wrong and develop a good self-concept. By setting limits and providing guidance for their children, parents help them become self-directed and capable of accepting responsibility for their actions. Parents strive to give their children a loving, safe, and supportive environment in which they can grow into responsible, healthy, happy, independent people.

Parenting skills will contribute to strong family relationships. Having this foundation will promote the physical, mental/emotional, and social health of all family members.

Teen Parenthood

While parenting is rewarding and full of joy, it is also demanding and full of challenges. Even some mature adults may find difficulty in adjusting to parenthood. The challenges to teens are even greater.

The reason most teens give for wanting a baby is to have someone to love them. They are unaware that it is only when a child is older that he or she is capable of giving unconditional love to a parent. In the early stages of a child's development, the parent is providing for the child's every need, as well as performing the many tasks associated with the child's care. Parents must be ready to give, rather than to receive, love. Teens are not prepared to handle the demands and responsibilities of raising a child.

Having a baby is tremendously rewarding when the child is brought into a loving, nurturing, and stable environment. However, with all the challenges of adolescence, most teens find the reality of raising a baby to be overwhelming. For most teens, having a baby is not a conscious decision; 78 percent of teen pregnancies are unplanned. A smaller percentage of teens plan their pregnancy, believing that a child will solve their other problems. They quickly find out that their problems have not disappeared and that they now face greater challenges.

▶ Teens may want to escape school or home, only to find they have no support system and a poor career outlook.

▶ Teens may think that having a baby will strengthen their relationship with their girlfriend or boyfriend. However, if a relationship is not strong enough on its own, having a baby will not solve that problem. In fact, the demands of parenthood may strain the relationship even further.

▶ They may want to prove to themselves or others that they are adults, only to learn how unprepared they are for adult responsibilities.

▶ A female teen may want to be the focus of attention, especially while pregnant, but she finds the baby will take all the time and attention.

Impact on Physical and Mental/Emotional Health

Pregnant females require special medical attention to ensure that they stay healthy and that they have a healthy baby. Regular prenatal care is essential, as is a healthful diet, adequate physical activity and rest, and a supportive, nurturing family and spouse. Teens are the least likely of all age groups to get the proper medical attention, and their diets frequently do not meet the nutritional demands of a growing fetus.

Teen mothers face a higher risk of medical complications such as early or prolonged labor, high blood pressure, and anemia. For teens younger than 15 years of age, the likelihood of complications is even greater. Babies of teen mothers are more likely to be born with health problems, including those associated with low birth weight. Teens also have more miscarriages.

For a mature, adult female, pregnancy can be a joyous, exciting time, but it can also be an emotionally stressful period. For a pregnant teen, this stress can become overwhelming because she often does not have the maturity or support she needs. Pregnancy is the most common reason teens drop out of school. In fact, only one-third of teen mothers finish high school. A teen dropout will have limited job opportunities and lower income.

Parenthood brings many responsibilities. The physical, emotional, and financial demands of a new baby can be overwhelming, especially for a teen.

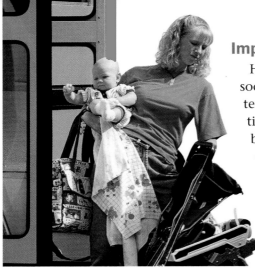

Impact on Social Health

Having a baby makes it impossible for teens to have an active social life. The 24-hour-a-day demands of a baby make it hard for teen parents to find time and healthy ways to meet their emotional needs. New parents find that their social activities become limited because of their new responsibilities. They often have to juggle difficult schedules and cannot spend time with friends and family as they once did. Their isolation, and their lack of preparation for the parental role, can leave teen parents feeling frustrated and depressed.

⚠ Only one-third of teen mothers finish high school.

DISCUSS. Ask students to discuss how their social lives would be affected by having a child.

Hands-On Health ACTIVITY

Advocating for Abstinence

Committing to abstinence will protect you and your peers from the physical, mental/emotional, and social consequences of teen pregnancy. In this activity, you will create a campaign to increase teen awareness about the importance and benefits of abstinence.

What You'll Need

- paper and pencil, pens, or markers
- computer and printer (optional)

What You'll Do

1. In groups of three or four, brainstorm ways to communicate the importance of teen abstinence. Examples may include flyers, posters, newspaper articles, public service announcements, or Web sites. Choose one medium, and develop strategies to carry out your campaign.

2. Analyze the importance and benefits of abstinence. Based on your analysis, create your campaign item and include strong messages about committing to abstinence. Make sure you discuss issues of emotional health and teen pregnancy.

3. Create your campaign, keeping in mind that it should appeal to teens. You might incorporate visual elements, slogans, or attention-getting headlines. Present your completed project to the class.

Apply and Conclude

As a class, carry out your campaign in your school or community.

Single Teen Parents

Most female teens who become pregnant do not marry the father of their baby, whether by her choice or his. Even if a teen couple marries, the marriage is more likely to fail than succeed. In either case, most babies of teen parents are raised in a **single-parent family**, or *a family that consists of only one parent and one or more children.*

Life for single teen mothers can be full of risks and challenges. Apart from being less likely to finish high school, teen mothers are dependent on others for financial support, are more likely to stay in a low-income bracket, and are unable to lead the life of a normal teen.

To cope with some of these problems, many teens who are single mothers live with their parents. Some parents can help with child care and provide the financial assistance, love, and support needed by both the mother and her infant. Many states require a teen parent to live with her parents if she is receiving financial aid from the government. If the parents are supportive, living at home is probably the best solution for everyone involved.

Single teen fathers also face difficulties. They do not have the maturity to provide the child with the necessary care, nurturing, and guidance. In addition, most states require a teen father to provide financial support for his child. He may then have to quit school to get a job. Without a high school diploma, however, he may always have difficulty getting a well-paying job, and college will be out of reach. Both his emotional and social health will likely suffer.

Deciding Not to Become a Teen Parent

Anyone can make the decision to delay becoming a parent. For teens, the decision to delay parenthood until they are mature and in a committed marriage provides the best

Health Minute
Reasons to Wait

Teens are not ready to become parents because:

► Teen pregnancies have an increased risk of medical complications.

► They are not emotionally ready for a pregnancy.

► They are not ready to give up their freedom to take on parenthood.

► They have not met their educational goals.

► They do not have stable marriages that foster the supportive, nurturing environment needed to raise a child.

► They do not have the financial resources to raise the child.

► They do not know the developmental needs of a child as he or she grows and matures.

DISCUSS. Have students discuss why they think most states require a teen father to provide financial support to a child.

 Teen fathers face many responsibilities, including providing financially for the child's care.

Couples who choose to remain abstinent can focus on their goals and dreams for the future.

EMPHASIZE. At this time, you may want to review the many benefits of abstinence, listed in Chapter 3.

opportunities for a happy future. Teen couples need to discuss their goals and feelings about the future with one another, communicating why they are not ready for marriage or children. In a healthy, loving relationship, teen couples will support one another's goals for the future. They are being responsible and realistic when they make the decision to wait until they are older to become parents. Mature, responsible teens also recognize that only abstinence will offer complete protection against pregnancy. When teens exercise their right to be abstinent, they are protecting their health and their future.

Lesson 2 *Review*

LESSON 2 REVIEW ANSWERS ARE FOUND ON PAGE TM28.

Reviewing Facts and Vocabulary

1. List reasons people give for deciding to have children.

2. Explain why pregnancy presents a health risk to a teen and her baby.

3. List some of the risks and challenges for a teen father.

Thinking Critically

4. **Analyzing.** Evaluate the effects of parenting and family relationships on physical, mental/emotional, and social health.

5. **Evaluating.** Describe the roles and responsibilities of parents in promoting healthy families. What do you think are the two most important responsibilities of being a parent? Why?

6. **Synthesizing.** What stressful situations might a teen experience as a result of an unplanned pregnancy? Why is it important for unmarried teens to practice abstinence?

Applying Health Skills

Refusal Skills. Using information on how pregnancy affects a teen's physical, mental/emotional, and social health, provide ways you could refuse engaging in sexual activity with a boyfriend or girlfriend. Write down at least two specific refusal statements.

CHAPTER 4 REVIEW ANSWERS ARE FOUND ON PAGE TM29.

➤ REVIEWING FACTS AND VOCABULARY

1. What is the most common reason for people to marry?
2. Describe people who have emotional and social maturity.
3. Identify four factors that can affect marital success.
4. Approximately what percentage of marriages end in divorce?
5. What is parenting? Describe the most basic functions a parent provides for a child.
6. How can a female teen's physical health be affected by pregnancy?
7. Name two adjustments a teen male may have to make if he becomes a parent.
8. What is the only sure way to prevent pregnancy until a person is ready to become a parent?

➤ THINKING CRITICALLY

9. **Analyzing.** What factors should be considered when making the decision as to whether a person is ready for marriage or whether one will choose to marry at all?
10. **Synthesizing.** Considering the factors that make up a successful marriage, what might be some reasons that marriages end in divorce?
11. **Comparing and Contrasting.** Make a comparison between a healthy marriage and an unhealthy marriage that you see in the media. Tell what characteristics make up each kind of marriage.
12. **Applying.** What goals have you set for yourself that you would have to delay or give up if you became a teen parent?
13. **Analyzing.** Why do you think some people make better parents than others? State reasons for your opinions.
14. **Comparing and Contrasting.** Compare and contrast what it would be like to have a baby as a single teen with what it would be like to have a baby after one is emotionally mature, married, and established in a career. Provide specific examples.

➤ APPLYING HEALTH SKILLS

15. **Advocacy.** Create a pamphlet that presents teens with the benefits of remaining abstinent and avoiding teen pregnancy. You can include reasons why being a teen parent is difficult as well as the actual demands of having and caring for a baby.
16. **Communication Skills.** Write a short story about a teen whose best friend wants to get married and have a baby before finishing high school. The teen should use effective communication skills to discuss with the friend the many risks of teen marriage and pregnancy. Include "I" statements, a respectful and caring tone of voice, and good listening skills.

BEYOND the Classroom

Parent Involvement

Research marriage customs. Using the Internet or library resources, find out about marriage customs in the United States compared to other countries. How are they different? How are they alike? Discuss these customs with your parents and other family members.

School and Community

Evaluate community resources. Research the amount of money it costs in your community to provide child care for a baby or for a toddler during a normal 40-hour work week. Find out whether the child-care centers provide care for sick children as well. Report your findings to the class.

Pregnancy and Childbirth

Quick Write

Using Visuals. A newborn baby's health is greatly affected by the care taken by the mother during pregnancy. What steps can a pregnant female take to ensure that both she and her baby are as healthy as possible?

Prenatal Development

VOCABULARY

fertilization
zygote
blastocyst
embryo
amniotic sac
placenta
umbilical cord
fetus
genes
genetic counseling

YOU'LL LEARN TO

• Explain fetal development from conception through pregnancy.

• Explain the significance of genetics and its role in fetal development.

• Discuss the importance of a healthful lifestyle before and during pregnancy.

QUICK START Why is it important to learn about fetal development? Write down your ideas in a brief paragraph.

Parenthood carries with it the responsibility to provide for a child's physical, mental/emotional, and social well-being. Although physical maturity occurs early in adolescence, the mental and emotional maturity that is needed for parenthood does not occur until adulthood. Teens do not have all the skills required to respond to the challenges of pregnancy and parenting.

Fertilization and Implantation

Pregnancy begins with conception, or **fertilization**—*the union of a single sperm and an ovum.* During sexual intercourse, the erect penis ejaculates hundreds of millions of sperm into the vagina. The sperm swim from the vagina through the cervix, into the uterus, and up the fallopian tubes. If an ovum is present in a fallopian tube, the first sperm that reaches the ovum can penetrate it. *A fertilized ovum* is called a **zygote**. After the zygote forms, it begins dividing, first into two cells, then four, then eight, and so on, as it travels down the fallopian tube to the uterus—a journey that takes three to four days. **Figure 5.1** on page 64 illustrates the path of a zygote.

EMPHASIZE. At this time, you may want to review the reasons presented in Chapter 4 discussing why people decide to have children.

In the uterus, the zygote becomes a **blastocyst**, *a ball of cells with a cavity in the center*. The blastocyst receives nourishment from secretions made by the uterine lining, or endometrium, for another few days before it begins to burrow into, or implant, in the uterine lining.

Embryonic Development

Six or seven days after fertilization, the blastocyst attaches itself to and becomes embedded in the uterine lining, which has been thickening to receive the blastocyst. This process takes a few days. *The implanted blastocyst* is called an **embryo**. Stages of embryonic development are shown in **Figure 5.2** on page 66.

The embryo grows rapidly during the next five weeks. By the sixth week, it is approximately 4/100 of an inch in size. The cells of the embryo begin to differentiate into three layers that will form the baby's organs and body systems. One layer becomes the respiratory and digestive systems; another develops into muscles, bones, blood vessels, and skin; and a third layer becomes the nervous system, sense organs, and mouth.

One of the first organs to develop is the brain. Neurons begin to develop about 18 days after fertilization. The central nervous system grows rapidly and the head takes shape about three weeks later.

As development continues, special membranes form around the embryo. One of these membranes becomes the **amniotic sac**, *a fluid-filled sac that surrounds the embryo*. The amniotic sac protects the embryo from outside impact and insulates it from temperature changes. The **placenta** is *a structure that forms along the lining of the uterus as the embryo implants*. The blood-rich tissues of the placenta

---

FIGURE 5.1

IMPLANTATION

Fertilization and implantation occur after an egg is released from the ovary.

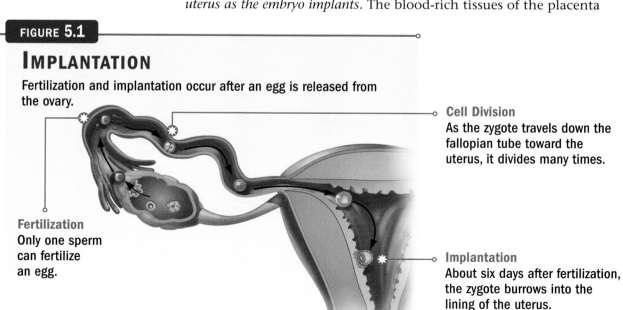

Cell Division
As the zygote travels down the fallopian tube toward the uterus, it divides many times.

Fertilization
Only one sperm can fertilize an egg.

Implantation
About six days after fertilization, the zygote burrows into the lining of the uterus.

transfer oxygen and nutrients from the mother's blood to the embryo's blood through the umbilical cord. The **umbilical cord** is *a ropelike structure that connects the embryo and the mother's placenta*. It grows to be about 20 inches long. Waste products leave the embryo's bloodstream through the umbilical cord and are then excreted from the mother's body along with her own wastes.

There is no direct exchange of blood between the mother and the embryo. Materials diffuse from one blood supply to the other through the umbilical cord.

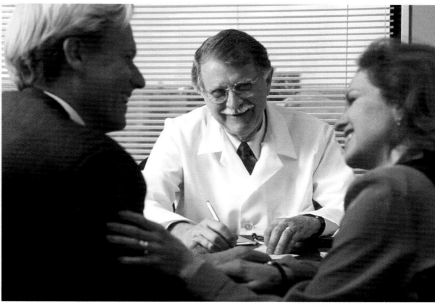

Fetal Development

By the end of the eighth week after fertilization, the major external features of the embryo are formed and the main organ systems are developing. *The developing baby from the end of the eighth week on* is called a **fetus**. At this point the fetus is only about 1 1/4 inches long, but it is recognizable as a human being. For the remaining 30 weeks of pregnancy, the fetus will continue to grow and develop. See **Figure 5.2** on the next page for the stages of fetal development.

Determining a Pregnancy

When fertilization occurs and the blastocyst stage is reached, a hormone called human chorionic gonadotropin (HCG) is released into the mother's bloodstream. This hormone stimulates the release of two other hormones, estrogen and progesterone, which maintain the uterine lining and suppress ovulation. Some HCG passes into the urine; a simple urine test can detect the presence and amount of HCG as early as one day after a missed menstrual period. This confirms whether or not a female is pregnant. The urine test can be performed at a doctor's office or in the home, using a store-bought pregnancy test. A radioimmunoassay is another type of pregnancy test that a doctor can perform. This test can detect HCG in urine or blood as early as a week *before* the expected menstrual period. A doctor will also perform an internal examination to confirm a pregnancy; changes in the cervix and the size of the uterus will be detected when a female is pregnant.

A physician should always confirm the results of a home pregnancy test. *What hormone is detected by pregnancy tests?*

EMPHASIZE. Stress to students that the structures that bring the embryo nutrients also bring in any alcohol, nicotine, or other drug the mother has used.

FIGURE **5.2**

STAGES OF EMBRYONIC AND FETAL DEVELOPMENT

The time from conception to birth is usually about nine full months, which are divided into three 3-month periods called trimesters. This figure describes the changes that take place during each trimester; the images show the development of the fetus in each trimester.

END OF FIRST MONTH	END OF SECOND MONTH	END OF THIRD MONTH
• Measures 3/16 inch long • Backbone formed • Arm and leg buds begin to form • Heart forms and starts beating	• Measures 1 1/4 inches long • Weighs 1/30 ounce • Arms and legs distinguishable, fingers and toes well formed • Eyes visible, eyelids fused • Major blood vessels form • Internal organs continue developing	• Measures 3 inches long • Weighs 1 ounce • Eyes, nose, and ears continue to develop • Heartbeat detectable • Limbs fully formed, nails appear • Urine starts to form

END OF FOURTH MONTH	END OF FIFTH MONTH	END OF SIXTH MONTH
• Measures 6 1/2 to 7 inches long • Weighs 4 ounces • Head proportionally large compared to body • Face more recognizable, hair forms on head • Bones hardening, joints begin to form • Body systems develop rapidly • External sex organs identifiable	• Measures 10 to 12 inches long • Weighs 1/2 to 1 pound • Lanugo (fine hair) covers body • Fetal movements felt by mother • Head more in proportion with rest of body	• Measures 11 to 14 inches long • Weighs 1 1/4 to 1 1/2 pounds • Eyelids no longer fused, eyelashes form • Skin wrinkled and pink

END OF SEVENTH MONTH	END OF EIGHTH MONTH	END OF NINTH MONTH
• Measures 13 to 17 inches long • Weighs 2 1/2 to 3 pounds • Fetus capable of surviving outside uterus • Body proportions more like that of full-term baby • Fetus assumes upside-down position	• Measures 16 1/2 to 18 inches long • Weighs 4 1/2 to 5 pounds • Fat deposits under skin make skin less wrinkled • In males, testes descend into scrotum • Bones of head soft	• Measures 20 inches long • Weighs 7 to 7 1/2 pounds • Additional fat deposits under skin • Lanugo (fine hair) falls off • Nails fully grown

Home pregnancy tests became available in the 1970s. Today they are the most popular home testing kit on the market, and one third of pregnant females use one. The test is similar to the one given in a doctor's office. However, research has shown that home pregnancy tests yield a high number of false negative results, which means that the test indicates a female is not pregnant when she really is. The unreliability of the test is mostly due to user error; thus, a female should see a physician to confirm the test results.

A Girl or a Boy?

The sperm determines a child's gender. The sperm and the ovum each contribute one set of 23 chromosomes during fertilization. A human being, therefore, has 23 pairs of chromosomes. One pair consists of specialized sex chromosomes, of which there are two types—X and Y. Ova always carry an X (female) chromosome; sperm can carry either an X or a Y. If a sperm carrying an X chromosome fertilizes an ovum, the combination is XX, and the child is female. If the sperm is carrying a Y chromosome, the combination is XY, and the child is male.

DISCUSS. Tell students that in Lesson 2 they will read about a test that can tell parents the gender of their baby. Ask students what other questions parents might have about their developing baby.

Genes and Heredity

The 23 pairs of chromosomes in the human body are made up of genes. **Genes** are *units of heredity that determine which traits, or characteristics, offspring inherit from their parents*. The genes we inherit determine traits such as height, hair color, and skin type.

For some traits, there are two types of genes—dominant and recessive. When both are present in an individual, the dominant gene will mask the effect of the recessive gene. For example, the gene for brown eyes is dominant and the gene for blue eyes is recessive. If a child inherits a gene for blue eyes from each parent, the child will have blue eyes; if a gene for brown eyes comes from each parent, the child's eyes will be brown. However, if a child inherits a gene for brown eyes from one parent and a gene for blue eyes from the other parent, the dominant gene for brown eyes will mask the effect of the recessive gene for blue eyes, and the child will have brown eyes.

EMPHASIZE. Tell students that although genes determine a person's inherited traits, not all such traits are either dominant or recessive. Some traits can be expressed as hybrids—a combination of the traits inherited from the mother and from the father. For example, the hair texture of a child with a curly-haired parent and a straight-haired parent can be wavy—a combination of the two.

Hereditary Diseases

Certain diseases can be passed from parent to offspring through genes. The genes for some hereditary diseases are dominant; thus, only one parent has to contribute that gene for his or her child to have the disease. For example, the gene for Huntington's disease, which causes the progressive loss of mental functions, is dominant. If a parent has this incurable disease, there is a fifty percent chance that he or she will pass the disease on to the child. In hereditary diseases for which the gene is recessive, both parents must contribute the gene for their child to have the disease. Parents can carry a recessive gene for the disease without having the disease themselves if they have a dominant gene to mask it. Cystic fibrosis is a recessive gene disorder. In this fatal disease, the body produces abnormally thick and sticky mucus in the lungs and other parts of the respiratory system.

Certain recessive gene diseases are only carried on the X chromosome. Because a female has two X chromosomes, she can have one dominant and one recessive gene and not have the disease. Because males have only one X chromosome, if they inherit a recessive gene for the disease, there is no paired dominant gene to mask it. Hemophilia and red-green color blindness are examples of this type of genetic disease.

CRITICAL THINKING. Tell students that genetic counselors study a variety of topics in science, health, and counseling. Ask students to list some of the topics a genetic counselor might study.

Genetic Counseling

Genetics is the study of heredity. **Genetic counseling** is *a process in which genetic histories of prospective parents are studied to determine the presence of certain hereditary diseases.* People's family histories can be mapped, and medical tests can be run to identify genetic or biochemical markers for certain hereditary diseases, such as Huntington's disease. Since most people don't show symptoms of this disease until later in life, genetic testing before pregnancy can help married couples make an informed decision about having children.

Lesson 1 Review

LESSON 1 REVIEW ANSWERS ARE FOUND ON PAGE TM31.

Reviewing Facts and Vocabulary

1. In a brief list, explain the major steps of fetal development from conception through pregnancy.
2. Describe the functions of the amniotic sac.
3. What will a doctor do to determine if a female is pregnant?
4. Does the father's sperm or the mother's ovum determine a child's gender?
5. What are *genes*? List some characteristics that are inherited.

Thinking Critically

6. **Synthesizing.** Explain why two parents with brown eyes may have a child with blue eyes.
7. **Analyzing.** In a short paragraph, briefly explain the significance of genetics and its role in fetal development.

Applying Health Skills

Communication Skills. Suppose someone tells you that she can't be pregnant because she took a home pregnancy test and the results were negative. What would you tell her?

Prenatal Care

VOCABULARY

prenatal
fetal alcohol
  syndrome
rubella
ultrasound
amniocentesis
chorionic villus
  sampling
birth defect

YOU'LL LEARN TO

- Analyze the harmful effects on the fetus of the mother's use of alcohol, tobacco, and other drugs, as well as environmental hazards such as lead and radiation.

- Explain the importance of the role of prenatal care and proper nutrition in promoting optimal health for both the baby and the mother.

- Explain how technology has impacted the health status of families by aiding in prenatal diagnosis of certain conditions.

 QUICK START List three things a pregnant female should do and three things she should not do to ensure the health of her baby.

Early signs of pregnancy vary and may be mistaken for the start of a menstrual period. Early testing is important because the sooner a pregnancy is confirmed, the sooner prenatal care can begin. **Prenatal** means *occurring or existing before birth.* Prenatal care increases the odds of a healthy pregnancy. As soon as a female knows she is pregnant, she should get prenatal care.

Characteristics of a Pregnancy

A normal pregnancy lasts about nine full months. Pregnancy can be divided into three trimesters, or periods of three months, each characterized by physical changes and symptoms.

   First Trimester. The breasts become fuller and tender, and blood vessels in the breasts become more prominent. The areola, the area around each nipple, darkens. Many females experience morning sickness—nausea or vomiting that occurs most frequently in the morning—and even mild exertion may bring on fatigue.

During the second trimester, most pregnant females feel healthy and energetic. *How long does a normal pregnancy last?*

Regular physical activity during pregnancy helps:

► prevent unnecessary weight gain.

► increase blood circulation.

► reduce fatigue and improve sleep.

► prepare the mother for the rigors of labor.

► improve mental health and well-being.

Second Trimester. The fetus grows enough to cause the abdomen to swell; the mother can detect fetal movements. Both appetite and blood volume increase. Any morning sickness usually subsides, and many females report feeling healthy and energetic during this time.

Third Trimester. Pregnancy is almost always visible by the third trimester. Most females will have gained 25 to 35 pounds by the time of delivery. Blood volume has increased by 30 to 40 percent, the mother's heart beats faster, and the uterus is stretched to many times its original size. After the birth, the uterus contracts to nearly its pre-pregnancy size. The growing fetus takes up enough room to crowd the mother's bladder, stomach, and lungs.

Mental/Emotional Changes

Hormonal changes cause many pregnant females to become more emotional or experience mood swings similar to those associated with premenstrual syndrome (PMS). In the first trimester, feelings can range from joy to fear to excitement. In the second trimester, hormonal shifts may cause forgetfulness. Some females may also have difficulty concentrating. As a pregnant female gains weight, her center of gravity changes and her ligaments loosen; this may cause her to feel more clumsy than usual. In the third trimester, worries about labor, delivery, and the health of the baby are all normal. Talking about these feelings with a caring partner, a physician, or another pregnant female can be helpful.

Common Discomforts

The growing fetus causes changes in a female's body that can bring on a range of discomforts during pregnancy. Urinary frequency increases, and many females experience leg cramps. Headaches, particularly in the first trimester, are also common. In the later months, back pain can result from increased weight in the front, and water retention causes swelling of the hands, ankles, and feet. Minor contractions and sleep problems may occur. Weight gain can result in the development of stretch marks, which a pregnant female may find unsightly. With the exception of stretch marks, these discomforts usually end after delivery.

Components of Prenatal Care

The care a female takes during pregnancy affects her own health, as well as that of her developing baby. Regular medical care; a well-balanced eating plan; regular physical activity; and avoiding harmful substances such as tobacco, alcohol, and other drugs are all responsible choices that a pregnant female can make.

Medical Care

The main component of prenatal care is a schedule of regular visits with an obstetrician or certified nurse-midwife. Both types of health care providers are trained in prenatal care and delivery of babies. The obstetrician or nurse-midwife takes a medical history and gives the pregnant female a complete physical examination, which includes blood and urine tests as well as a pelvic examination. Regular visits are usually scheduled once a month through the seventh month, every two weeks in the eighth month, and weekly in the ninth month. At each visit, the mother's weight and blood pressure will be taken, her urine tested, her abdomen measured, and (from week 12) the fetal heartbeat will be monitored.

Nutrition and Physical Activity

A pregnant female needs to consume more nutrients to ensure the health of the developing fetus. She needs extra protein for her own strength and for the development of the placenta, amniotic sac, and fetal brain. She needs extra calcium to build strong fetal bones and teeth, vitamin E for tissue growth and red blood cells, and iron—also for red blood cells. Inadequate iron intake can lead to fatigue and possibly anemia. Doctors recommend that all pregnant females take prenatal vitamins to ensure that they are getting adequate nutrients.

Another necessary nutrient is folic acid. This B vitamin is a critical part of spinal fluid and helps close the tube that contains the central nervous system. This neural tube forms 17 to 30 days after conception, so neural tube defects can occur before a female knows that she is pregnant. Health care professionals suggest that all females of childbearing age consume 400 to 600 micrograms of folic acid daily to prevent neural tube defects.

For females who are at a healthy pre-pregnancy weight, gaining more than 35 pounds during pregnancy can be a health risk for both mother and baby. Daily caloric intake should only increase by about 300 calories, and those additional calories should come from nutritious foods, including those rich in calcium and protein.

Physical activity is important during pregnancy. In a normal pregnancy, most activities a healthy female did before she became pregnant can be continued. Walking and swimming are particularly good activities during pregnancy.

EMPHASIZE. A pregnant female should consult with her doctor about her physical activity routine to ensure that she and her developing baby will not have any problems.

Good nutrition ensures that a pregnant female receives the nutrients required for proper fetal development.

Medical Complications

In a normal pregnancy, there are no major problems. Proper prenatal care can help identify and treat medical complications when they do arise.

Rh Factor in Blood. Rh factor is a protein on the surface of red blood cells. About 85 percent of people have this antigen in their blood and are called Rh+ (Rh positive). Those who do not have it are Rh– (Rh negative). When an Rh– person receives Rh+ blood, their blood builds up antibodies against the Rh antigen. If an Rh– mother and an Rh+ father have an Rh+ baby, the mother's antibodies can cross the placenta and attack the baby's red blood cells. Treatment of the mother with a serum known as Rh immune globulin can prevent the buildup of antibodies, but the problem must be diagnosed early to avoid serious fetal complications.

Pregnancy-Induced Hypertension and Preeclampsia. The mother's blood pressure normally rises a bit around the seventh month, but about 5 percent of pregnant females develop prolonged high blood pressure, or pregnancy-induced hypertension (PIH). High blood pressure can be dangerous to both the mother and the baby, so it is monitored carefully.

If PIH is accompanied by sudden weight gain, severe swelling from water retention, and/or protein in the urine, the female has a condition known as preeclampsia. If untreated, this condition can lead to many health problems for the mother, ranging from blurred vision and headaches to convulsions and coma. Preeclampsia can also cause stunted growth and mental retardation in the fetus. First-time mothers in their early teens or those over 35 are most at risk. Complete bed rest and medication can increase the chances of a full-term delivery, but sometimes the baby must be delivered early to protect both mother and baby.

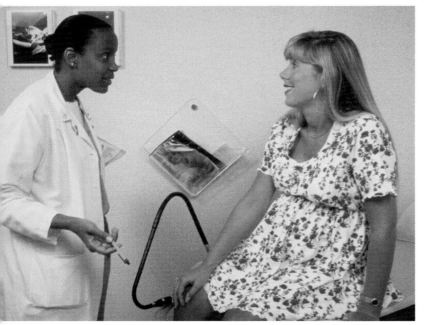

▼ **Regular prenatal checkups can help identify potential complications during pregnancy.** *Why is it important for a pregnant female to have her blood pressure checked regularly?*

Dangers to the Fetus

Although mother and baby do not directly share any blood, substances in the mother's bloodstream cross the placenta and enter the fetus's blood. No medication should be taken without medical advice, and alcohol, tobacco, and illegal drugs should be avoided entirely.

Tobacco. Tobacco use is harmful to both mother and baby. Babies born to females who smoke can have lower birth weights, heart and brain abnormalities, and cleft lips and palates. Smoking has been linked to higher fetal and infant mortality rates, as well as sudden infant death syndrome (SIDS), a condition in which a seemingly healthy baby dies for no apparent reason. Secondhand smoke also poses a health risk, according to the American Lung Association, which states that pregnant females exposed repeatedly to secondhand smoke have an increased risk of having a low birth-weight baby.

Alcohol. Fetal alcohol syndrome is *a condition of physical, mental, and behavioral abnormalities that can result when a pregnant female drinks alcohol.* Problems include low birth weight, general weakness, impaired speech, poor coordination, stunted growth, cleft palate, facial and heart defects, mental retardation, poor attention span, inability to understand the consequences of actions, and hyperactivity. Fetal alcohol syndrome does not occur unless alcohol is consumed; the safest decision for pregnant females and those considering pregnancy is not to drink any alcoholic beverages.

Medications and Drugs. All medications and supplements must be approved for use during pregnancy by a health care professional. This includes prescription and over-the-counter products, as well as those labeled "natural" or "herbal." Many seemingly benign substances can harm the fetus.

All illegal drugs are unsafe and can cause serious health problems in the fetus, including mental retardation, respiratory problems, visual and hearing disabilities, learning and emotional problems, low birth weight, and even death. A baby can also be born addicted to a drug and have to go through the painful and dangerous process of withdrawal.

Caffeine. Some studies suggest that consuming caffeinated products during pregnancy may pose health risks to the fetus. Coffee, tea, chocolate, cola drinks, and some other kinds of soft drinks may contain caffeine. Many females choose to avoid caffeine during pregnancy to help ensure their baby's health.

Rubella (German measles). Rubella is *a contagious disease caused by a virus.* Symptoms include a rash, swollen glands, and joint pain, particularly in adults. Most pregnant females are immune to the disease, either through vaccination or because they had the disease as children. Nevertheless, about 20 percent of females of childbearing age are not immune to rubella. If a pregnant female contracts rubella, especially during the first trimester, her fetus may develop severe birth defects. These include vision and hearing loss, heart defects, and mental retardation. Rubella infection can cause miscarriage, the spontaneous expulsion of a fetus that occurs before the twentieth week of pregnancy. It may also cause stillbirth, the expulsion of a dead fetus from the body after the twentieth week of pregnancy. If a female contracts rubella after 20 weeks of pregnancy, birth defects are rare.

Responsibility. Pregnant females have a responsibility to protect the developing fetus by avoiding the use of harmful substances such as tobacco, alcohol, and other drugs. **Create a pamphlet explaining why it is especially important for a female to avoid using harmful substances during pregnancy.**

GOVERNMENT WARNING: (1) ACCORDING TO THE SURGEON GENERAL, WOMEN SHOULD NOT DRINK ALCOHOLIC BEVERAGES DURING PREGNANCY BECAUSE OF THE RISK OF BIRTH DEFECTS. (2) CONSUMPTION OF ALCOHOLIC BEVERAGES IMPAIRS YOUR ABILITY TO DRIVE A CAR OR OPERATE MACHINERY AND MAY CAUSE HEALTH PROBLEMS.

 Alcohol consumption during pregnancy can cause many serious health problems in the fetus.

Other Dangers. Direct exposure to radiation can harm a developing fetus, so it is best to avoid routine X rays such as those taken by a dentist. If X rays are necessary, however, as in the case of a broken bone, a protective apron can be placed over the abdomen to shield it from radiation. Maternal exposure to lead can also endanger a fetus, causing developmental defects and mental deficiency when lead in the mother's bloodstream passes through the placenta to the fetus's blood. One common source of lead is paint in buildings built before 1978, when lead-based paint was banned. Maternal lead exposure can also cause higher rates of miscarriage, premature birth, and stillbirth.

EMPHASIZE. Tell students they will learn more about STDs in Chapter 7 and HIV/AIDS in Chapter 8.

Sexually Transmitted Diseases

Sexually transmitted diseases (STDs) are diseases spread through sexual contact; some are very harmful to a fetus and newborn (see **Figure 5.3**). Because of the serious threat posed by STDs, pregnant females are tested for these diseases at the first prenatal visit with their health care professional. Some STDs can be cured, but others can only be treated. Females who know they have an STD should seek treatment before they become pregnant.

FIGURE 5.3
EFFECTS OF STDS ON THE FETUS AND INFANT

STD	Time of Transmission	Harm to Fetus/Infant	Treatment
Chlamydia	During delivery	Eye infections, blindness, pneumonia	Antibiotics
Gonorrhea	During delivery	Eye infections, blindness, general infections	Antibiotics
Herpes	During delivery	Attacks nervous system, can cause encephalitis (inflammation of the brain) and death	No cure; antiviral medications can minimize outbreaks; cesarean delivery can protect baby
HPV	During pregnancy/ delivery	Development of warts on genitals or anus or in the throat	Antibiotics, surgery, chemotherapy
Syphilis	During pregnancy	Bone and tooth deformities, nervous system damage, brain damage, death	Antibiotics before the fifth month can often prevent harm to fetus
HIV	During pregnancy/ delivery	Abnormal heart structure and function, suppressed immune system	No cure; AZT helps prevent transmission from mother to child

Tests During Pregnancy

Prenatal tests may be ordered to see if a fetus is at risk for various health problems. Sometimes a problem can be treated before the baby is born.

Ultrasound

The fetus can be seen in the uterus by using **ultrasound**, *a test that produces an image on a screen by reflecting sound waves off the body's inner structures.* The embryo can be seen by four weeks after fertilization, and the fetal heartbeat can be identified at five weeks. To produce an image, an instrument called a transducer is moved across the abdomen; a computer translates the reflections into images on a monitor. Ultrasound can be used throughout pregnancy as a diagnostic tool for assessing fetal position and development.

An ultrasound allows a fetus to be observed without exposing either the mother or the fetus to the radioactivity of X rays.

Amniocentesis

Amniocentesis is *a procedure that reveals chromosomal abnormalities and certain metabolic disorders in the fetus.* Ultrasound is used to determine the position of the fetus, and then the doctor inserts a long needle through the abdomen and into the amniotic sac and removes 1 to 2 tablespoons of amniotic fluid. The fluid contains living cells from the fetus that are tested for chromosomal abnormalities and also reveal the gender and age of the fetus. Amniocentesis is usually performed 16 to 20 weeks after fertilization, and the procedure carries a small risk of miscarriage—about 0.25 percent to 0.50 percent, according to the Centers for Disease Control and Prevention. Because of this risk, amniocentesis is usually recommended only for those females who have an increased risk of having a child with chromosomal or genetic abnormalities. Factors that may contribute to these abnormalities include the following:

▶ The mother is 35 years of age or older.

▶ The mother has had a previous child or fetus with a birth defect.

▶ There is a family history of certain chromosomal or genetic disorders.

Chorionic Villus Sampling

Another *test used to reveal genetic disorders and fetal age and gender* is **chorionic villus sampling** (CVS). In this procedure, a thin

How does amniocentesis enable doctors to learn a fetus's gender?

The living fetal cells in the amniotic fluid removed during amniocentesis are cultured, or grown in a laboratory. During the subsequent analysis of the chromosomes for abnormalities, the chromosomes are paired and identified. The complement of sex chromosomes indicates the sex of the fetus—XX for a female, XY for a male.

tube is inserted through the vagina and the cervix. A small sample of chorionic villi, tissue attached to the sac that contains the fetus, is removed. The test is usually done between 10 and 12 weeks after a female's last menstrual period; results are available within 10 days. CVS is slightly more likely than amniocentesis to cause miscarriage. Like amniocentesis, CVS is usually only offered to pregnant females with an increased risk of giving birth to a child with genetic or chromosomal abnormalities. Some parents choose CVS because the test can be performed earlier than amniocentesis.

THINKING SKILLS. Ask students how prenatal testing might help the survival of a baby born with a genetic birth defect.

Birth Defects

A **birth defect** is *an abnormality in the structure or function of the body that is present at birth.* According to the March of Dimes, approximately 150,000 infants are born with birth defects each year in the United States. There are more than 4,000 known birth defects. Birth defects can be caused by abnormal genes or by environmental factors. Environmental factors include maternal exposure to toxins, maternal diseases, and maternal substance abuse. They also include problems that may arise during delivery, such as when the fetus does not receive an adequate supply of oxygen. Many physical defects, such as cleft lip and clubfoot, are visible at birth. Mental defects such as retardation, cerebral palsy, and brain dysfunction may not be observed until the child is older. Other conditions that are present at birth may not be apparent until the child is several months to a year or more old. Sickle-cell anemia and cystic fibrosis are examples of such defects.

Lesson 2 *Review*

LESSON 2 REVIEW ANSWERS ARE FOUND ON PAGE TM32.

Reviewing Facts and Vocabulary

1. List two physical changes that occur during each trimester.

2. How can alcohol, tobacco, other drugs, and environmental hazards harm a fetus?

3. What is *fetal alcohol syndrome*?

4. Name two tests that can be done during pregnancy to see if the baby is at risk for a genetic or chromosomal abnormality.

Thinking Critically

5. **Synthesizing.** Explain the importance of the role of prenatal care and proper nutrition in promoting optimal health for both the baby and the mother.

6. **Analyzing.** Briefly explain how technology has impacted the health status of families by aiding in prenatal diagnosis of certain conditions.

Applying Health Skills

Refusal Skills. Suppose you have an older sister who is pregnant. She has told you that some of her friends are trying to convince her that it's okay to drink alcohol during her pregnancy. Explain to her why she needs to use her refusal skills, and give her some suggestions of ways to say "no" effectively.

Childbirth

VOCABULARY
labor
episiotomy
cesarean birth
birthing centers

YOU'LL LEARN TO
- Identify and explain the stages of labor.
- Explain how breastfeeding promotes optimal health for the baby.

QUICK START Briefly explain why a pregnant female needs to have regular exams by a health care professional.

A t the end of the pregnancy, the hormone oxytocin causes uterine contractions that begin to pull open the cervix. This is the beginning of the birthing process.

Stages of Labor

L abor is *the process by which contractions gradually push the baby out of the uterus and into the vagina to be born.* It has three stages.

First Stage of Labor

Contractions gradually open the cervix to a diameter of about 4 inches. This process of dilation is the first, and usually longest, stage of labor. The pressure of the baby's head against the amniotic sac during this stage or the next one usually causes the sac to rupture. Known as water breaking, this occurrence causes about a pint of amniotic fluid to be released from the vagina. This stage may last for 12 hours or more.

Second Stage of Labor

When the cervix is fully dilated, the mother feels an urge to push. She uses muscles to aid the contractions in pushing the baby's head through the cervix and into the vagina.

CRITICAL THINKING. Ask students why it might be helpful for a new mother-to-be to talk about labor to a female who has had children.

After a baby is delivered, the doctor or nurse-midwife places the child in the mother's arms.

What is a breech birth?
A breech birth is a birth in which the baby enters the vagina with the buttocks or feet first. The dangers of a breech birth are related to the delivery of the head last. Because the umbilical cord precedes the head, the cord can become compressed when the head moves through the birth canal, cutting off the baby's supply of oxygen. Because the head is delivered quickly, sudden pressure changes on the skull can result in brain hemorrhage, causing brain damage.

When the baby's head crowns, or is visible at the vaginal opening, the mother continues pushing until the entire baby is delivered. This stage generally lasts from $1/2$ hour to 2 hours. Rather than risk tearing the tissues around the vaginal opening, a doctor will sometimes perform an **episiotomy**, *an incision made from the vagina toward the anus to enlarge the opening for delivery of a baby*. The incision is stitched back together after the birth.

Third Stage of Labor

The final stage of labor lasts about 20 minutes. Contractions separate the placenta from the uterine wall and expel the placenta from the uterus and out of the body through the vagina. The detached placenta is called the afterbirth.

Delivery by Cesarean

In a **cesarean birth**, *a method of childbirth in which a surgical incision is made through the abdominal wall and uterus*, the baby is lifted out through the incision. The incidence of cesarean section (C-section) has risen dramatically in recent years, accounting for almost 23 percent of U.S. births. Some C-sections are performed because the baby is not positioned correctly or does not progress into the vagina, or because the mother's pelvic structure makes a vaginal delivery dangerous or even impossible. C-sections are also used to avoid transmission of certain STDs to the baby when it passes through the vagina. A pregnant female should discuss her views on C-section with her health care provider before labor begins.

Medication During Labor

Some females deliver their babies without pain medication. For those who need pain relief, several medications can be used. Some females find that pain relief drugs relax them and help them deal with the contractions. Others find the drugs make them too drowsy to concentrate and participate fully in the birth. The effect of pain medications on the baby depends on the amount administered and how close to delivery the drug is given to the mother. If, for example, medications are given shortly before birth, the baby may be drowsy or have difficulty breathing.

When total pain relief is needed, an epidural block is used. Medication injected through a tube inserted between the vertebrae into the spine provides total numbness from the waist down. Epidurals are used during C-sections and some vaginal births. General anesthesia, where the female is unconscious, is used almost exclusively for high-risk cesarean births.

After Delivery

A baby can nurse as soon as he or she is born. While the mother is not yet producing milk, her breasts secrete colostrum, a low-fat, high-carbohydrate, protein-rich fluid. Colostrum is easy to digest and has a laxative effect on the newborn.

After a few days, the breasts begin to produce milk. Both colostrum and milk contain antibodies from the mother's system; therefore, breastfed babies get fewer illnesses than babies who are not breastfed. Breast milk is nutritionally ideal for almost all babies, it doesn't cost anything, it's easier to digest than formula, and it's

▲ Birthing rooms are designed so that a female can remain in the same hospital room for labor, delivery, and recovery.

Real-Life Application

Health Information in the News

Recently, news organizations noted an interesting and significant trend in teen pregnancies in the United States, based on statistics from the National Center for Health Statistics (a branch of the Centers for Disease Control and Prevention). The graph below reflects some of these statistics for pregnancies among females 15 to 19 years of age from 1940 to 2000.

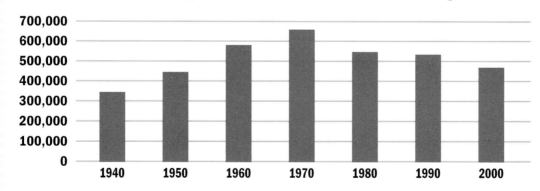

Number of Pregnancies in Females 15–19 Years of Age

ACTIVITY

Work in groups of two or three to answer the following questions: How would you describe the overall trend(s) since 1940? In which year were pregnancies highest among this age group? Approximately what percentage decrease occurred between 1970 and 2000? If the trend continues, approximately what number would you expect to see in 2010? Discuss possible reasons for the decline of the last three decades. Be prepared to present your findings to the class.

DISCUSS. Ask students to discuss why some parents may choose a birthing center for the delivery of their baby.

always ready. Babies aren't allergic to breast milk, but many are allergic to formulas based on cow's milk or soy protein. For these reasons, most pediatricians recommend breast milk over formula.

Childbirth: Options and Trends

Many parents choose to educate themselves about the process of childbirth. They attend classes in birthing methods such as Lamaze™ or the Bradley Method®. Most doctors and nurse-midwives recommend that expectant parents attend some type of childbirth classes where they will learn what to expect at each stage of labor and delivery. The father, a close friend, or a relative learns to play the role of coach; the mother learns relaxation and breathing techniques that enable her to cope with the pain of labor and perhaps have a medication-free delivery. The goal is to make the experience less mysterious and as painless as possible.

Another choice parents can make is where to have their baby. A popular option today is **birthing centers**, *facilities that have homelike settings, are separate from a hospital, and offer medication-free births.* Birthing centers are usually available only for low-risk pregnancies because they are not designed for emergencies, although centers are often located near hospitals in case an emergency arises. Many hospitals now offer their own birthing centers within the hospital.

Lesson 3 Review

LESSON 3 REVIEW ANSWERS ARE FOUND ON PAGE TM34.

Reviewing Facts and Vocabulary

1. Briefly describe what occurs during each of the three stages of labor.
2. Explain what an *episiotomy* is and why it is used.
3. What is a *cesarean birth*?
4. When parents attend classes in birthing methods, what is the goal?

Thinking Critically

5. **Synthesizing.** Explain how breastfeeding promotes optimal health for the baby.
6. **Analyzing.** How is a prepared childbirth course helpful to an expectant mother?

Applying Health Skills

Stress Management. In addition to helping a pregnant female prepare for childbirth, classes in birthing methods also teach the expectant mother how to relax. Why might stress interfere with labor and delivery? What are some stress-management techniques a female could use throughout her pregnancy?

CHAPTER 5 REVIEW ANSWERS ARE FOUND ON PAGE TM35.

► REVIEWING FACTS AND VOCABULARY

1. What is *fertilization*? How is it related to pregnancy?
2. When is the developing fetus's heartbeat detectable?
3. What happens during genetic counseling?
4. Describe the physical and mental/emotional changes a female may experience during her second trimester of pregnancy.
5. How can tobacco use affect a developing baby?
6. List one reason why a pregnant female would have an ultrasound.
7. About how many known birth defects are there? What can cause them?
8. Describe the second stage of labor.
9. What is taught in childbirth preparation classes?
10. What is a birthing center?

► THINKING CRITICALLY

11. **Synthesizing.** How are the placenta and umbilical cord integral to the nourishment of the embryo and fetus?
12. **Analyzing.** A pregnant female notices a sudden weight gain. She visits her doctor, who finds that her blood pressure is very high. What condition would the doctor likely suspect? What other symptoms will the doctor check for? Explain your answers.
13. **Evaluating.** Suppose a pregnant female carries the gene for a genetic birth defect. Would you suggest that she undergo amniocentesis, chorionic villus sampling, or neither? Explain your choice.
14. **Analyzing.** Why might a doctor recommend a cesarean birth instead of allowing labor and delivery to progress naturally?

► APPLYING HEALTH SKILLS

15. **Advocacy.** Create a pamphlet that encourages females to seek medical care when they are pregnant. List the reasons why medical care is important throughout the pregnancy as well as during labor and delivery. Work to make your pamphlet as attractive and informative as possible.
16. **Practicing Healthful Behaviors.** Review the information presented in this chapter. Talk with a pair of prospective parents. Discuss with them what you have learned about healthful behaviors during pregnancy and the birth process.

BEYOND the Classroom

Parent Involvement

Medication options. Do research at the library or on the Internet to learn more about the pros and cons of using various medications during labor and delivery. Discuss this issue with your parents or guardians and ask what their views are on the subject.

School and Community

Treatment options. Research the symptoms of postpartum depression at the school or community library. Identify ways that these symptoms can be treated. Present your findings to the class.

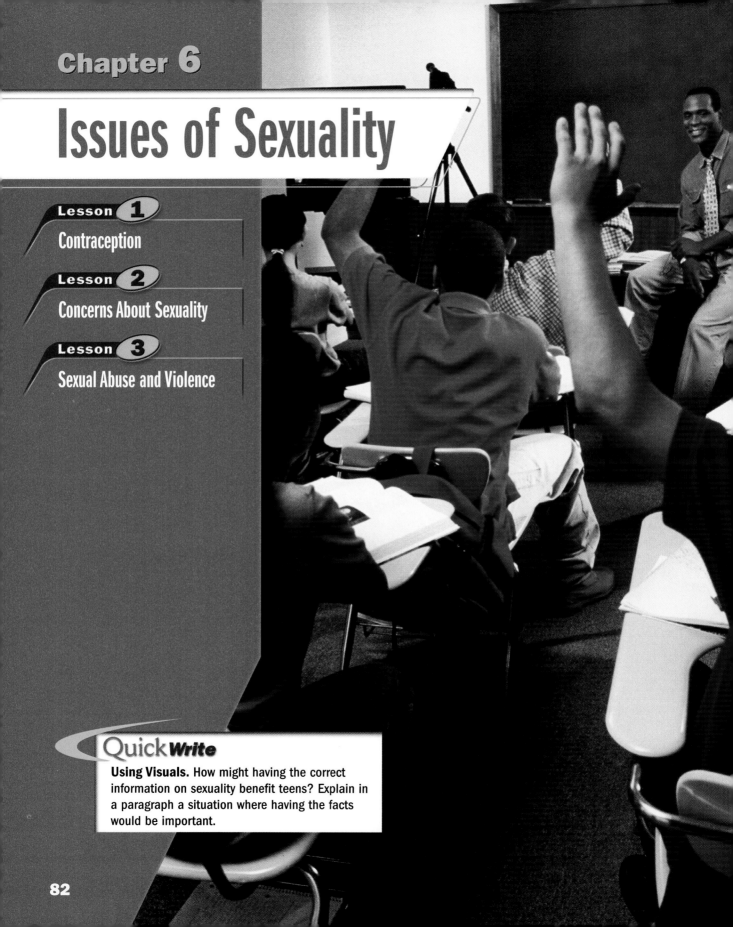

Chapter 6

Issues of Sexuality

Quick Write

Using Visuals. How might having the correct information on sexuality benefit teens? Explain in a paragraph a situation where having the facts would be important.

Lesson 1

Contraception

VOCABULARY

withdrawal
contraception
condom
spermicide
fertility awareness
    methods (FAMs)
oral contraceptives
diaphragm
cervical cap
contraceptive implant
sterilization
vasectomy
tubal ligation

YOU'LL LEARN TO

- Analyze the effectiveness and ineffectiveness of contraceptive methods and the role they play in the prevention of pregnancy and STDs.

- Analyze the importance of abstinence from sexual activity as the preferred choice of behavior for unmarried persons of school age.

- Discuss abstinence from sexual activity as the only method that is 100 percent effective in preventing pregnancy and STDs, including HIV/AIDS.

 QUICK START How much do you know about contraception and STD prevention? On a piece of paper, list three contraceptive methods that you believe also offer some protection against STDs.

In the United States, almost one million teens become pregnant each year; most of these pregnancies are unplanned. Factors such as lack of correct information, belief of incorrect information, alcohol and drug use, negative peer pressure, and portrayals of risk-free sex in the media all contribute to this serious but preventable problem.

DISCUSS. Ask students for examples of reliable and unreliable sources of information about contraception. Discuss how students can be certain they have correct information.

Facts About Pregnancy Prevention

Whenever sperm are in or near the opening of the vagina at the same time that an ovum is present in a fallopian tube, pregnancy is possible. It is difficult even for mature women to know exactly when ovulation occurs each month, and sperm can live for 3 to 6 days in the female reproductive tract. Because there is no reliable way for an adolescent to know when ovulation is going to occur, there is no period free of the risk of pregnancy. Here are

Douching is a process used to cleanse the vagina; it is *not* a way to prevent pregnancy.

- Sperm left in or near the opening of the vagina cannot be rinsed out. In fact, the liquid inserted into the vagina during douching actually pushes the sperm upward toward the cervix—the entrance to the uterus.
- Many doctors suggest that females avoid douching for a couple of reasons. First, douching is unnecessary for cleansing purposes because the vagina cleanses itself. Second, douching can alter the vagina's natural environment and leave a female vulnerable to infection.

some important facts about pregnancy and pregnancy prevention.

▶ Females can ovulate before their first menstrual period, so a teen can become pregnant before she knows she is fertile.

▶ Sperm normally live for 12 to 48 hours inside the female reproductive tract, but they can live for as long as 6 days.

▶ Because the timing of ovulation varies and sperm can live inside the female reproductive tract for several days, fertilization is possible even if sexual intercourse occurs during the female's menstrual period.

▶ It only takes one sperm and one ovum for pregnancy to occur, and any act of sexual intercourse, even the first, can result in pregnancy.

▶ Sperm cannot be flushed out of the vagina by urinating; urine leaves the body through the urethra, not the vagina.

▶ Sperm cannot be flushed out of the vagina by douching; in fact, douching may push sperm farther into the vagina, making fertilization more likely.

▶ If sexual intercourse occurs while standing up, in a hot tub, or just for a few minutes, pregnancy can occur.

▶ **Withdrawal**, *the male's removal of the penis from the vagina before ejaculation*, is *not* a method of preventing pregnancy. Some sperm from the ejaculatory duct may be present in the clear fluid released by Cowper's glands before ejaculation. The male does not know when this pre-ejaculate fluid is being released. Also, if semen is deposited near the outside of the vagina, sperm can travel through semen and vaginal secretions into the vagina. Withdrawing at the height of sexual pleasure also requires a great deal of control at a time when the abilities to think clearly and act responsibly are strained.

Contraception

The word **contraception** means *prevention of pregnancy*. As you read about the various nonprescription and prescription forms of contraception, remember that the only 100 percent effective method for preventing pregnancy is abstinence from sexual activity.

Nonprescription Birth Control Methods

Nonprescription means that a prescription or examination by a health care professional is not necessary. Nonprescription methods of birth control can be purchased at most drugstores and supermarkets.

The Condom

A **condom** is *a thin sheath of latex, plastic, or animal tissue that is placed on the erect penis to catch semen.* It is a physical barrier to the passage of sperm into the vagina and toward the ovum. Some condoms are also coated with a **spermicide**, *a chemical that kills sperm.* For any condom to be an effective contraceptive, it must be used correctly.

▶ The condom must be unrolled onto the erect penis before there is any contact with the vagina.

▶ There must be a space between the tip of the penis and the end of the condom to leave room for semen. If there is no space, the condom could break, allowing semen out. Some condoms have a built-in receptacle at the tip.

▶ As soon as ejaculation occurs, the male must hold the condom in place and remove the penis from the vagina; once the penis softens, the condom can slip off and release semen into the vagina.

Female condoms fit inside the vagina. To be effective, they must be inserted before the penis comes in contact with the vagina.

Petroleum jelly or other petroleum-based products should never be used with a latex condom because these products can dissolve latex and weaken the condom. Since heat also destroys latex, such condoms should not be stored in the glove compartment of a car or carried in a wallet for any length of time—they should be stored in a cool, dry place. Condoms should never be reused; they should be used only once and then discarded.

Contraceptive Foams, Jellies, Creams, and Suppositories

Contraceptive foams, jellies, and creams contain a spermicide. They are applied with a plunger-type applicator deep in the vagina near the cervix. To be effective, the foam, jelly, or cream must not be applied more than 30 minutes before intercourse. After intercourse, it is important that the female not bathe or douche; the spermicide must remain in place to be effective.

Which types of male condoms protect against STDs?
Latex condoms offer the best protection against most STDs, including HIV infection. When used correctly—before there is any sexual contact—they block the exchange of body fluids that may be infected with the pathogens that cause STDs. Plastic condoms are also effective, but they are still being studied. Animal tissue condoms do not offer effective protection against STDs because natural pores in the tissue allow passage of some infectious agents, including HIV. Keep in mind that condoms must be used each and every time sexual intercourse takes place, and instructions must be followed exactly.

EMPHASIZE. Tell students that for condoms to be effective protection against unplanned pregnancy and STDs, it is important to follow the instructions on the package.

EMPHASIZE. Explain to students that methods using spermicide and birth control pills cannot prevent transmission of STDs. In order to protect against STDs, such methods must be used in conjunction with the male condom.

Condoms are one nonprescription method of contraception. Others include contraceptive suppositories and contraceptive foams, jellies, and creams.

CRITICAL THINKING. Ask students why some adult couples might choose fertility awareness methods as their form of birth control.

Couples must receive special training from a health care professional to learn how to use FAMs as a form of contraception. *Why is this method not recommended for teens?*

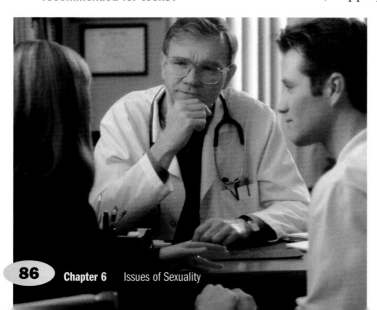

Contraceptive suppositories are bullet-shaped and are usually inserted with an applicator. Unlike foams, jellies, and creams, suppositories take about 15 minutes to dissolve and release the spermicide. Nevertheless, they must not be inserted more than 30 minutes before intercourse if they are to effectively kill sperm. Although the chemicals in some suppositories may be irritating to vaginal tissues, douching or bathing is not recommended because it decreases the effectiveness of the spermicide.

Fertility Awareness Methods (FAMs)

Fertility awareness methods (FAMs) are *methods of contraception that involve determining the fertile days of the female's menstrual cycle and avoiding intercourse during those days.* Fertile days are from six to seven days before ovulation through two to three days after ovulation. To use these periodic abstinence methods correctly, couples must receive special instruction, keep careful records, and plan ahead. With typical use, these methods are about 80 percent effective. Because a teen female's menstrual cycle is usually irregular, it is nearly impossible to determine when she ovulates each month. Thus, FAMs are a particularly ineffective form of contraception for young people.

The basal body temperature method involves the female taking and recording her temperature every morning before rising. A basal thermometer is used to identify the slight rise in the female's temperature that occurs at ovulation and continues until she gets her period. Tracking basal body temperature for several months gives an indication of when ovulation normally occurs; however, many women—especially teens—have irregular cycles that cannot be charted reliably.

The cervical mucus method requires checking the mucus secretion from the cervix daily and recording changes in its characteristics. Cloudy and sticky for most of the cycle, cervical mucus becomes clear, slippery, and stringy a few days before ovulation. Recording changes in cervical mucus over a number of months can help a female determine when in her cycle she normally ovulates.

With all FAMs, once the timing of ovulation has been determined, the couple abstains from intercourse from six to seven days before ovulation until about three days after ovulation. FAMs are entirely dependent on the female having an established, regular menstrual cycle. These methods of contraception provide no protection against STDs.

Prescription Birth Control Methods

Prescription forms of birth control require a visit to a licensed health care professional to obtain a prescription, a fitting, or another related procedure. These methods include

▶ oral contraceptives (birth control pills).

▶ the diaphragm and cervical cap.

▶ contraceptive implants.

The Birth Control Pill

Oral contraceptives, or birth control pills, are *hormone pills that, taken correctly, create changes in the female body that prevent pregnancy.* A female must visit a health care professional to obtain a prescription for birth control pills. She will need to provide a personal and family medical history, have her blood pressure taken, and be given a pelvic exam and Pap test. If the doctor feels that a female can safely take the pill, she will receive a prescription and complete instructions.

The pills most often prescribed contain synthetic versions of estrogen and progesterone—two hormones normally produced by the ovaries. The pill must be taken every day to be effective. With perfect use, which means that no pills are ever missed, the pill is 99.9 percent effective. For the first month on the pill, and if a female misses a dose, she should use another method of birth control. Certain medicines also decrease the effectiveness of the pill; females taking the pill should inform their health care provider before taking any other medications.

Although much has been written about the pill and its side effects, they are very individual. For this reason, females should have regular medical checkups and notify a physician if any problem or unusual change occurs. Some females experience unpleasant side effects, such as nausea, breast tenderness, weight gain, mood swings, and breakthrough bleeding, especially for the first few months after beginning to take the pill. A few develop serious health problems, such as high blood pressure, blood clots, and stroke. Some females, such as those who experience migraine headaches or have diabetes or high blood pressure, should not take the pill. The pill is also not recommended for females who smoke or who are severely overweight.

The Diaphragm and Cervical Cap

Worn inside the female's vagina, the diaphragm and the cervical cap are physical barriers to the passage of sperm through the cervix into the uterus and toward the ovum. A contraceptive **diaphragm** is *a soft latex cup with a flexible rim that covers the entrance to the*

EMPHASIZE. Along with being an effective form of birth control, the pill may provide some protection against ovarian and endometrial cancers. Women who use the pill have fewer ectopic pregnancies.

Diaphragms and cervical caps are barrier methods of contraception—they keep the sperm and ovum apart; contraceptive implants prevent ovulation.

Did You Know

Other forms of prescription birth control for females include the following.

• The injection, which consists of a progesterone-like hormone, is given four times a year by a health care professional. Also known as "the shot," the injected hormone works by preventing the ovaries from releasing an ovum each month. Each injection provides three months of protection; effects are reversible after stopping the injections. When used properly, the injected hormone is 99.7 percent effective in preventing pregnancies.

• The contraceptive patch and a hormone shot that is given monthly also prevent ovulation.

cervix. A **cervical cap** is *a thimble-shaped, soft latex cup that fits snugly onto the cervix.* The cervical cap is smaller than the diaphragm. Spermicidal jelly or cream is applied inside the cup of both the diaphragm and the cervical cap before insertion. Petroleum jelly must never be used because it weakens the latex.

Diaphragms and cervical caps come in different sizes. A female needs to have a pelvic examination so that the health care professional can measure her and prescribe the correct size for her body. She also needs instructions for insertion and removal of the device, and an opportunity to practice placing and removing it under medical supervision. A female should be refitted for a diaphragm or a cervical cap if she has delivered a baby, had a miscarriage or an abortion, or either gained or lost more than 15 pounds. The diaphragm or cap must be used correctly every time intercourse takes place.

▶ **Using the Diaphragm.** Before inserting the diaphragm, it must be covered with contraceptive jelly or cream. It should completely cover the cervix when in place. If intercourse is repeated, more spermicide must be inserted in the vagina without removing the diaphragm. The diaphragm must be left in place for at least six hours after the last act of intercourse. Leaving it in place for longer than 24 hours, however, increases the risk of infection.

▶ **Using the Cervical Cap.** Before inserting the cervical cap, the inside of the cup must be one-third full of spermicide. As with the diaphragm, it is important to check that the cervix is completely covered. The cap must stay in place for at least 8 hours after intercourse, but never for longer than 48 hours.

After use, the diaphragm or cap is washed with soap and water, rinsed, and patted dry. Before it is stored in its plastic container, it should be checked for holes by holding it up to a light and carefully examining its surface. A diaphragm or cap with even a tiny hole or tear is not an effective birth control method and must be replaced at once.

The Contraceptive Implant

The **contraceptive implant** is *a birth control procedure that involves insertion of six small rods about the size of a paper matchstick under the skin of a female's upper arm.*

To insert the rods, a doctor first uses a local anesthetic to numb the area. He or she then makes a small incision and implants the rods under the skin. This procedure, which is generally painless, takes about ten minutes. The rods release small amounts of hormones that prevent the ovaries from releasing an ovum each month. There is no daily routine to follow or action to take before intercourse. Protection lasts for about five years but is reversible at any time. Side effects vary. Some females experience weight gain, hair loss, headaches, upper arm discomfort, and/or increased PMS symptoms from contraceptive implants. Other females using the implants find that PMS symptoms improve. This method of birth control provides no protection against STDs.

DISCUSS. Emphasize in discussion with students the importance of understanding that many contraceptive methods covered here do not protect against STDs.

Real-Life Application

Health Information from Charts and Graphs

You can get useful information from charts and graphs when you know how to read them. The chart below is based on information available from Planned Parenthood. What type of information does this chart give you? Read all the legends and keys to get the maximum information from the chart.

Pregnancies Based on Methods of Birth Control (in first year of use)

# of Pregnancies per 100 Females in Typical Use

Legend:
- Abstinence***
- Contraceptive Implant*
- The Pill*
- Condom (male)**
- Condom (female)**
- Diaphragm*
- Cervical Cap (females who have not given birth)*
- Cervical Cap (females who have given birth)*
- Vasectomy
- Tubal Ligation
- Spermicide
- No Method

Source: Planned Parenthood
* No protection against STDs
** Some protection against STDs
*** Total protection against STDs

ACTIVITY

Based on the information in the chart, write a summary of the birth control methods covered. In your summary,

• group methods with similar levels of effectiveness.

• address the effectiveness of methods that do not fall into any specific group.

• identify which method is the least effective, which is the most effective, and which offers the most protection against STDs.

Sterilization

Sterilization is *a surgical procedure that makes a male or female incapable of reproducing.* See the illustrations in **Figure 6.1**.

VASECTOMY

A **vasectomy** is *a sterilization procedure for males.* It is a method of permanent birth control that works by keeping sperm out of the semen. During a vasectomy, each vas deferens is cut and sealed. Sperm are still produced but are absorbed by the body rather than being mixed into the semen. Because sperm are already present in the ducts beyond the points where the vas deferens were cut, vasectomy is not immediately effective. Normally, a male's semen will not be totally free of sperm until 15 to 20 ejaculations have occurred after surgery. Another birth control method must be used to prevent pregnancy until the semen is totally free of sperm. A semen analysis can show whether or not sperm are present.

Vasectomy does not in any way affect masculinity or the ability to have an erection, to ejaculate, or to experience sexual pleasure. The procedure is 99.9 percent effective. Males who someday may want to have children should not have a vasectomy; surgery to reverse the procedure is costly and has limited success. Vasectomy does not protect the male or the female against STDs.

TUBAL LIGATION

Tubal ligation is *a sterilization procedure for females.* The fallopian tubes are cut and tied or clamped to prevent sperm from reaching the ova. An ovum is still released each month, but it cannot be

In a vasectomy, each vas deferens is cut and sealed. During a tubal ligation, the fallopian tubes are cut and tied or clamped to prevent sperm from reaching the ova.

FIGURE 6.1

STERILIZATION METHODS

Vasectomy (males)

- ureter
- bladder
- prostate
- vas deferens
- vasectomy site
- epididymis
- testis

Tubal ligation (females)

- site for tubal ligation
- uterus
- fallopian tube
- ovary

fertilized and it dissolves within the body. Tubal ligation is a more involved procedure than vasectomy and requires a hospital stay. Complications following surgery may include cramps, heavier periods, breakthrough bleeding, and pelvic pain. Tubal ligation is 99.5 percent effective and is considered permanent. Surgery to reverse the procedure has met with limited success in restoring fertility. As with vasectomy, this method of birth control offers no protection against STDs, including HIV/AIDS.

Abstinence

A bstinence from sexual activity is the *only* method that is 100 percent effective in preventing unplanned pregnancy and the transmission of STDs, including HIV. Abstinence from sexual activity is the preferred choice of behavior for all unmarried persons of school age. By making a decision to abstain from sexual activity, you demonstrate maturity and a positive self-concept, and you preserve your chances of fulfilling your goals for the future.

EMPHASIZE. At this time, you may choose to review the "Benefits of Abstinence" section of Chapter 2, Lesson 2.

 Lesson 1 *Review*

LESSON 1 REVIEW ANSWERS ARE FOUND ON PAGE TM37.

Reviewing Facts and Vocabulary

1. Name three nonprescription methods of birth control.

2. Explain the proper way to use a male condom.

3. List four possible side effects of the birth control pill.

4. Define *sterilization* and identify a sterilization procedure for males and one for females.

Thinking Critically

5. **Analyzing.** Using a scale of one to five (with one being the most effective), analyze the effectiveness and ineffectiveness of the following contraceptive methods in preventing pregnancy: diaphragm, birth control pill, spermicide, abstinence, male condom.

6. **Synthesizing.** Analyze the effectiveness and ineffectiveness of the following contraceptive methods in preventing STDs: diaphragm, birth control pill, FAMs, abstinence, condom.

Applying Health Skills

Advocacy. Create a poster that compares various methods of contraception and shows why abstinence from sexual activity is the preferred choice of behavior for unmarried persons of school age and is the only birth control method that is 100 percent effective in preventing pregnancy and STDs, including HIV/AIDS.

Concerns about Sexuality

VOCABULARY

masturbation
homosexual
heterosexual
stereotype
abortion

YOU'LL LEARN TO

• Explain why some people masturbate.

• Describe myths regarding sexual orientation and discuss how to show consideration and respect toward others.

• Distinguish between spontaneous and induced abortion.

QUICK START Fold a piece of paper in half, lengthwise. On the left side of the paper, list questions or concerns about sexuality that you would feel comfortable discussing with a friend. On the right, list questions or concerns that you would rather not discuss with anyone. Review your lists after the lesson is complete. Consider talking with a trusted adult about any remaining questions or concerns.

Some people find discussing sexual issues uncomfortable, and therefore avoid such discussions. Lack of accurate information can cause unnecessary concern and confusion, and reluctance to get the facts may lead to misunderstandings that can have a significant impact on health. Knowing the facts not only will help you understand your growth and development, but also will help you make decisions that promote your health and protect you from certain diseases and other conditions.

CRITICAL THINKING. Ask students why some people have claimed that masturbation has harmful effects.

Masturbation

Masturbation means *touching one's own genitals for sexual pleasure.* Some people believe that masturbation is a natural part of growth and development, while others believe it is wrong and unhealthy. In the past, people who considered masturbation harmful and wrong made many claims about the consequences of such activity to encourage young people to avoid it. Today we know that masturbation does not cause blindness, insanity, acne, hair growth on the palms of the hands, physical weakness, or decreased athletic ability. However, masturbation may go against some people's principles and religious beliefs.

People masturbate to relieve sexual tension. For some people, masturbation is a responsible alternative to sexual intercourse; it relieves sexual tension but poses no risk of pregnancy or contracting STDs. Other people choose not to masturbate for a variety of reasons.

Masturbation is a personal issue and a private activity that should not affect a person's social growth or ability to make friends. Problems can arise, however, with any behavior that becomes obsessive (extremely habitual) or that interferes with other areas of a person's life. There may be psychological stress if people feel guilty about what they are doing or find it difficult to think about or focus on other people and activities. If masturbation becomes a problem, it can be helpful to discuss the concern with a parent, guardian, or another trusted adult.

Sexual Orientation

Sexual orientation is the recognition of a gender preference with regard to sexual attraction. A **homosexual** is *someone who is sexually attracted to people of the same gender.* A **heterosexual** is *someone who is sexually attracted to people of the opposite gender.* Homosexuality is an emotionally charged issue in our society.

There are many myths about homosexuality. One myth is that a person is homosexual because he or she is not yet interested in the opposite gender. This is not true. A person may develop an interest in the opposite gender much earlier or much later than some of his or her friends. Another myth is that a person is homosexual just because his or her closest friend is of the same gender. It is not only normal, but also healthy, to have close, caring friendships with peers of the same gender. Another common myth is that someone who has not had sexual contact—especially if the person is male—is homosexual. This is untrue. Having or not having sexual contact has nothing to do with sexual orientation.

It is also a myth that you can identify homosexuals or heterosexuals by appearance and mannerisms. The idea that all homosexuals act one way and all heterosexuals act another is based on stereotypes. A **stereotype** is *an idea or image held about a group of people that represents a prejudiced attitude, over-simplified opinion, or uninformed judgment.*

DISCUSSING. Have students discuss why stereotypes are damaging.

Throughout the life cycle, it is normal and healthy to have close friendships with peers of the same gender; such friendships have no bearing on sexual orientation.

Respect. When you show empathy and tolerance for people who are different from you, you are demonstrating respect. **Imagine you overhear your nine-year-old sibling telling a friend that someone is homosexual and you are concerned that he or she is stereotyping. Write what you would say to him or her.**

People should not be judged by the way they look. Incorrect assumptions can be made when people are labeled because of their appearance or behavior. The most important point to remember is that every person is unique and is worthy of consideration and respect as an individual.

What causes homosexuality? Some research suggests that there is a genetic component, a different chemical environment during fetal development, or a different balance of hormones at birth. Some studies also point to influences in the home and society during a child's formative years. Almost certainly there is no single reason why some people are homosexual.

A teen who thinks that he or she may be homosexual may experience a lot of stress. Concerns about how family and friends will accept the situation are reasonable, and fears about being teased or even attacked are not unfounded. Some teens, however, may also believe that they are the only ones who are attracted to members of the same gender. This belief can lead them to feel isolated and depressed. It can be helpful for adolescents who have issues about their sexual orientation to speak with a trained counselor. He or she can help them talk about their feelings and concerns and provide them with facts. Remember that factual information can help you develop a healthy attitude toward the challenges facing adolescents.

> Teens in schools across the nation are finding ways to promote tolerance and respect.

Pregnancy Termination

Pregnancies end prematurely for many reasons. *Any termination of a pregnancy* is called an **abortion**. When a pregnancy ends spontaneously, from natural causes, it is called a spontaneous abortion or miscarriage. Miscarriages are most common in the first trimester of a pregnancy. It is estimated that as many as 25 percent of all pregnancies end in miscarriage, many without the females even knowing that they had been pregnant. Miscarriage may occur for a variety of reasons, including a hormonal deficiency, a faulty ovum or sperm, or a weak endometrium. When miscarriage occurs, it is usually early in the pregnancy and is something over which the female has little or no control.

A medically terminated pregnancy, also called an induced abortion, purposely ends a pregnancy. An induced abortion is a medical procedure and must be performed by qualified professionals in a medical setting. The issue of induced abortion is highly controversial and it should never be considered a method of birth control. You should discuss with your parents their feelings about induced abortions.

Lesson 2 Review

LESSON 2 REVIEW ANSWERS ARE FOUND ON PAGE TM38.

Reviewing Facts and Vocabulary

1. Define the terms *homosexual* and *heterosexual*.
2. What is a *stereotype*?
3. What does research suggest regarding why some people are homosexual?
4. Explain what the two types of abortion are.

Thinking Critically

5. **Analyzing.** Why can stereotypes harm people?

6. **Synthesizing.** Why do you think people have such strong viewpoints about induced abortion?

Applying Health Skills

Communication Skills. Write a paragraph explaining what you would say to a friend who tells you that he or she is concerned about his or her sexual orientation because he or she has not started dating yet.

Sexual Abuse and Violence

VOCABULARY

sexual abuse
incest
rape
**acquaintance
  rape**
date rape

YOU'LL LEARN TO

• Analyze issues surrounding sexual abuse and incest.

• Describe situations that can lead to acquaintance rape and date rape.

• Analyze the importance of healthy strategies that prevent physical, sexual, and emotional abuse, including date rape.

QUICK START Suppose that a close friend confides in you that a trusted friend of her family has been making sexual advances toward her. Your friend tells you that this person has warned her not to tell anyone, saying that no one would believe her if she did. Write down what you would tell your friend to do.

Whenever any act of sexual contact is forced on a person, it is an act of violence. Acts of violence involving sexuality affect many people in our society. While in some cases a stranger attacks a person and forces sexual contact on him or her, more often the attacker is someone the victim knows. The force that is used against the victim may be physical, but when the attacker is familiar to the victim, the force is likely to be emotional.

EMPHASIZE. The incidence of sexual abuse cuts across all socioeconomic and ethnic lines.

Sexual Abuse and Incest

Sexual abuse is *any sexual contact that is forced on a person against his or her will*. Sexual abuse is always illegal, it is always a crime, and it is never the victim's fault. It can affect people of all social, economic, and ethnic groups. Males and females of any age may be victims of sexual abuse. Children and teens who are victims of sexual abuse frequently know their abuser as someone they trusted. Such a person takes advantage of the young victim's trust or uses his or her position of authority to pressure the victim into sexual activity.

If the sexual abuser is related to the victim, the abuse is called **incest**—*sexual contact between family members who cannot marry by* *law*. Incest can involve parents or stepparents, aunts, uncles, brothers, sisters, or any other relative. Whenever the sexual abuser is a trusted adult, the pressure used against a young victim is commonly persuasive or emotional rather than physical. The adult may discourage the victim from telling anyone about the abuse by using statements such as:

▶ "This will be our special secret."

▶ "You'll break up the family."

▶ "I'll go to jail and it'll be your fault."

▶ "No one will believe you, and I'll say you're lying."

▶ "Your parents will be very mad at/disappointed in you."

These types of statements are very persuasive because they can provoke guilt and anxiety in young people. Out of fear, loyalty, or obedience, many victims remain silent about the abuse. Some victims may believe they caused the abuse or that they were at fault because they did not resist. Unfortunately, children may not understand or know that forced sexual contact is wrong. Remember that, without exception, sexual abuse is the fault of the abuser, not of the victim.

What to Do About Sexual Abuse

The first and most important step a victim of sexual abuse can take is to tell someone about the abuse. This is particularly difficult to do if the abuser is a family member, a friend of the family, or a leader within the community. People might not believe the victim because they can't imagine this person as a sexual abuser. If this happens, the victim should keep trying until he or she finds someone who takes him or her seriously. A victim of abuse can find help from a parent or guardian, a doctor, the school nurse, a school social worker, a guidance counselor, a trusted teacher, a close friend's parent, or the local police. Both the victim and the abuser need to receive professional help and counseling.

Rape

Rape, or *any form of sexual intercourse that takes place against a person's will*, is illegal. As with other types of sexual abuse, rape is an act of violence, not of passion. Victims of rape can be males or females of any age; in the United States, there were about 300,000 victims of rape and related crimes in the year 2001. Females account for 90 percent of rape victims, one in ten victims is male, and about 44 percent of victims are under the age of 18.

Many rapes of female teens are either **acquaintance rape**, *rape by someone the victim knows*, or **date rape**, *rape by someone the*

▲ Victims of abuse should seek help from parents, guardians, or a medical professional.

CRITICAL THINKING. Ask students why it is important for both the abuser and the victim to get help.

EMPHASIZE. Males often think that they cannot be sexually assaulted because they are strong and able to protect themselves. Discuss the fact that such assaults are perhaps more frequent because they are often not reported.

Avoid Becoming a Victim of Date Rape Drugs

The term "date rape drugs" is used to describe the drugs Rohypnol, GHB, and Ketamine, which rapists sometimes give to unknowing victims, usually by dissolving the drug in a drink. These drugs cause blackouts and memory loss, so that a victim becomes helpless and is unaware of what is happening.

To protect yourself against date rape drugs:

► Never accept any kind of drink from someone you don't know well and trust completely.

► Never accept a drink you have not seen poured or made.

► Do not leave your drink unattended.

► Do not accept a drink from a large public beverage container, such as a punch bowl.

► If you feel ill, ask for help immediately and publicly.

---

victim is dating. A victim of date or acquaintance rape may think it wasn't rape because she knows the male, or she may feel responsible for a rape because she didn't resist soon enough or firmly enough. Whenever any sexual act is forced on a person against his or her will, it is rape, and rape is never the victim's fault.

For many victims, fear that they will be blamed or not believed may prevent them from telling anyone about the rape. Because our society gives males the message that they are strong and should be able to protect themselves, a male victim of rape may find discussing the rape especially difficult.

Fear, anger, grief, shame, and embarrassment keep many victims from reporting rape. However, one of the best ways to reduce the occurrence of rape is for all victims to report it. Although the reporting procedure can be difficult, embarrassing, or upsetting, an unreported rape leaves the rapist uncaught, unpunished, and free to rape again.

Protecting Yourself Against Rape

Follow these commonsense guidelines to protect yourself against rape.

► Do not go places alone; stay with a group.

► If you do go somewhere alone, tell someone your plans.

► Walk briskly, be aware of your surroundings, and look alert.

► Stay in well-lit areas where other people are present.

► Have your keys out and ready as you approach your home or car.

► Lock all doors and keep windows up when driving; check inside and under a parked car before getting in.

► Keep windows and doors locked at home; never open your door to strangers or acquaintances that you do not know well.

► If you have car trouble, stay inside your locked car. If someone offers to help, ask him or her to call for assistance.

► Keep a cell phone in your purse or car.

► If you are being followed, go to a public place. Run, scream, and make as much noise as you can.

Protecting Yourself Against Date Rape

Use these tips to protect yourself against date rape.

► Do not go on blind dates alone. Know the person you are going out with, and learn about his or her friends and reputation.

- Go on group dates the first few times you're out with a new person.

- Do not go to isolated places on a date.

- Tell someone at home where you will be and when you plan to return.

- Take money with you, including change, so that you can make a phone call or take a taxi home if a situation becomes unsafe. If you have a cell phone, bring it.

- Do not use drugs or alcohol. If your date is using these substances, leave immediately.

EMPHASIZE. Remind students that rape is never the victim's fault.

Health Skills Activity

Decision Making: Dealing with an Unsafe Dating Situation

Carrie was home baby-sitting her little sister one Saturday night when the phone rang.

"Carrie? Thank goodness you're home."

"Betsy, what's wrong? Where are you?"

"I'm in Will's bathroom," Betsy whispered. "I'm so scared!"

"What's going on?"

"Will's parents are out for the night. We started kissing, but then Will got angry with me when I didn't want to go any farther than that. What should I do, Carrie? Will's waiting for me to come back. I need your help."

What Would You Do?
Put yourself in Carrie's shoes. Apply the six steps of the decision-making process to help Carrie decide how to help her friend.

1. State the situation.
2. List the options.
3. Weigh the possible outcomes.
4. Consider values.
5. Make a decision and act on it.
6. Evaluate the decision.

What to Do if You or Someone You Know Is Raped

Being raped is a terrifying experience. If you or someone you know has been raped, do the following.

▶ Tell a parent, close friend, or someone else you trust; ask for emotional support.

▶ Notify the police immediately. Ask for a sex crimes officer of the same gender as you are.

▶ Do not take a shower, change clothes, or douche. These actions can remove evidence that the police will need.

▶ Get a physical examination as soon as possible. Most rape victims have injuries that need medical attention. A hospital emergency room is equipped to handle rape cases and can take semen samples to help identify the rapist. Emergency room personnel may give the victim an antibiotic to fight possible infections and can provide counsel about the possibility of becoming pregnant or contracting an STD or HIV/AIDS.

▶ Find a counselor, therapist, or support group to help work through the emotional trauma of rape. It is normal for a rape victim to have a wide range of feelings; talking about fears and concerns is an important way to start healing from the emotional wounds. Many communities have a rape crisis center with counselors who are specially trained for this purpose.

 Lesson 3 *Review*

LESSON 3 REVIEW ANSWERS ARE FOUND ON PAGE TM39.

Reviewing Facts and Vocabulary

1. Define the term *sexual abuse.*

2. Why might a victim of sexual abuse or incest remain silent about the abuse?

3. What is the first and most important step a victim of sexual abuse can take?

4. List three things you can do to protect yourself against date rape.

5. Why shouldn't a victim of rape take a shower or change clothes afterward?

Thinking Critically

6. **Analyzing.** What is the difference between sexual abuse and incest?

7. **Synthesizing.** List five situations a person could be in that might put him or her at risk of being a victim of rape. Suggest ways this person can make better decisions to protect himself or herself.

Applying Health Skills

Practicing Healthful Behaviors. Analyze the importance of healthy strategies to prevent physical, sexual, and emotional abuse, including date rape. Create a pamphlet that features tips for teens to follow to protect themselves against rape. Be sure to use appealing design elements and colors to illustrate your pamphlet. Distribute the pamphlets throughout your school.

CHAPTER 6 REVIEW ANSWERS ARE FOUND ON PAGE TM40.

➤ REVIEWING FACTS AND VOCABULARY

1. Why is douching not an effective method of contraception?
2. What is *withdrawal*? Is it an effective method of preventing pregnancy?
3. Explain how contraceptive suppositories work.
4. List two Fertility Awareness Methods of contraception.
5. Name three prescription forms of birth control.
6. What are *oral contraceptives*?
7. For how long does a contraceptive implant provide protection from pregnancy?
8. What is the term for a pregnancy that ends spontaneously?
9. What is *rape*?
10. Explain the difference between acquaintance rape and date rape.

➤ THINKING CRITICALLY

11. **Synthesizing.** If you received conflicting information about contraception, where would you go to find the correct information?

12. **Comparing.** Compare vasectomy and tubal ligation in terms of the actual procedure, recovery, and effectiveness.
13. **Synthesizing.** Using facts from this chapter, analyze the importance of abstinence from sexual activity as the preferred choice of behavior for unmarried person of school age.
14. **Analyzing.** Why do you think some people believe false information about sexual issues, such as masturbation or homosexuality?
15. **Evaluating.** How might a person who has sexually abused a child be helped by a counselor who specializes in such cases?

➤ APPLYING HEALTH SKILLS

16. **Accessing Information.** Create a directory of all the resources available in your community to help people with contraception, STDs, sexual abuse, and rape.
17. **Analyzing Influences.** How might movies that feature people making unsafe decisions about sexual activity negatively affect a teen audience?

✦ *BEYOND* the Classroom

Parent Involvement

Discuss safety strategies. With a parent or guardian, discuss ways that teens can reduce the risk of date or acquaintance rape.

School and Community

Help for victims. Do research at the library and talk to a counselor about treatment of victims of rape and incest. Write a report about the treatment process and add suggestions that you feel might help victims. Suggest ways that present treatment methods might be improved.

Sexually Transmitted Infections

Quick Write

Using Visuals. List sources of information teens can access on STDs. In addition to medical professionals and pamphlets, what other sources could you use to find accurate information?

Common Sexually Transmitted Infections

VOCABULARY

sexually transmitted infections (STIs)
sexually transmitted diseases (STDs)
human papillomavirus (HPV)
genital warts
chlamydia
pelvic inflammatory disease (PID)
gonorrhea
genital herpes

YOU'LL LEARN TO

- Describe the relationship between high-risk behaviors, including alcohol and drug use, and the risk of contracting a sexually transmitted disease.

- Recognize and discuss abstinence from sexual activity as the only method that is 100 percent effective in preventing sexually transmitted diseases or infections.

- Develop and analyze strategies to prevent the spread of sexually transmitted diseases.

➔ *QUICK START* In the center of a piece of paper, write the words *sexual contact*. Draw a circle around these words. Make a word web around the circle by drawing lines outward from the circle and writing the names of all the sexually transmitted diseases that come to mind. Write one way to avoid sexually transmitted diseases.

Great strides have been made in controlling the spread of many communicable diseases, but the incidence of sexually transmitted diseases continues to rise. **Sexually transmitted infections (STIs)**, or **sexually transmitted diseases (STDs)**, are *infections that spread from person to person through sexual contact*. There are more than 25 known STDs, many of which are difficult to track because people who have them may not exhibit symptoms. Other cases are not reported because people do not seek treatment due to shame, fear, or ignorance.

DISCUSSING. Explain that the CDC has recently used the term sexually transmitted *infection* in an effort to encourage more people to seek testing treatment for an infection.

STDs: Widespread Among Teens

An estimated 15 million people contract one or more STDs in the United States each year; one-fourth of these new cases are in teens. Currently in the United States, more than 65 million people have an incurable STD. Why do these epidemics persist and grow? One reason is that many STDs have no symptoms. Other STDs have a lengthy delay between infection and symptoms, and still others have symptoms that go away while the disease continues to damage the body. Many people also remain uneducated about STDs or believe that they are somehow immune.

Sexually active teens are at high risk for contracting STDs because teens who are sexually active are likely to engage in one or more of the following high-risk behaviors:

▶ Engaging in any form of sexual intercourse—including oral, anal, or vaginal sexual contact—without using any barrier protection method, such as condoms

▶ Using alcohol and other drugs, which causes people's behavior to change and their inhibitions to lower

▶ Being sexually active with more than one person at a time or over time

▶ Choosing high-risk partners who have a history of being sexually active

▶ Choosing high-risk partners who have a history of intravenous drug use

▶ Choosing a partner who seems to be low risk but really isn't

Only Abstinence Can Prevent STDs

Some teens may think that only people who are very sexually active get STDs. The truth is that anyone who has sexual contact with an infected person is at risk, and since a person does not always show symptoms of an STD, sexual activity of any kind with any person is risky. The good news is that because STDs require sexual contact for transmission, they can be prevented. Choosing to practice abstinence is a healthy, responsible, and mature decision for teens. Here are some guidelines that teens can follow to avoid risky situations.

▶ Set limits and communicate them to your date before you go out.

▶ Stay in public places when you go on dates.

- Use refusal strategies if you are pressured to engage in sexual activity.

- Never use alcohol or illegal drugs.

- Choose friends and dates who practice abstinence.

- Protect your food and beverages while on a date to avoid the risk of date rape drugs.

Common STDs in the United States

In this lesson you will learn important facts about some of the most common STDS—human papillomavirus, chlamydia, gonorrhea, and genital herpes. The most important fact to remember is: The primary way these STDs are spread is through any form of sexual intercourse, including vaginal, oral, or anal sex. Teens who practice abstinence eliminate their risk of contracting STDs.

Human Papillomavirus

Human papillomavirus (HPV) is *a virus that causes genital warts and warts on other parts of the body.* While chlamydia is the most commonly *reported* STD in the United States, health experts believe that genital HPV infection is the most commonly *contracted* of all the STDs. Though many cases go unnoticed and unreported, it is thought that about 5.5 million people contract the disease each year in the United States. An estimated 20 million Americans already have the disease.

Like many STDs, HPV infection often does not have symptoms. The most easily recognized symptom is **genital warts** (also called venereal warts), which are *soft, moist, pink or red swellings that appear on the genitals.* Genital warts often grow in clusters and may spread into large masses. When present in females, the warts are found on the vulva, in the vagina, on the cervix, or around the anus. In males, genital warts are found on the penis, scrotum, groin, thigh, or around the anus. Genital warts are found only rarely in the mouth or throat.

There are more than 100 types of HPV, most of which are harmless and cause benign conditions such as skin warts on other parts of the body. About 30 types of HPV are spread through oral, anal, or vaginal sexual contact. Certain types of genital HPV infection are linked to cervical cancer, including some that are also associated with cancers of the vulva, anus, and penis.

▼ **Barrier protection such as condoms are not effective in preventing HPV. The virus can be transmitted without the presence of genital warts.**

EMPHASIZE. As you discuss genital herpes and HIV, tell students they will learn more about HIV/AIDS in Chapter 8.

HPV is most commonly diagnosed by an examination of genital warts; doctors sometimes use an acidic solution to make warts more visible. Genital warts may disappear by themselves or can be removed by laser or by being frozen, burned, or cut off. An antiviral drug can also be injected directly into larger warts, and other topical treatments may be used. Removal of the warts does not eliminate the virus, however. The warts often recur and the virus remains in the body for life.

Chlamydia

Chlamydia is *an STD that is caused by the bacterium Chlamydia trachomatis*. It is not only the most commonly reported bacterial STD in the United States, it is also the most commonly reported infectious disease. About 2 million Americans are currently infected; 3 million become infected each year. Forty percent of reported cases are among people 15 to 19 years old.

Despite the fact that it is easily cured, chlamydia has become one of the most dangerous STDs. This is because it often goes undiagnosed. About 75 percent of women and 50 percent of men with the disease have no symptoms. During the early stages of infection, a very small percentage of females develop an abnormal vaginal discharge or a burning sensation when urinating. Males with symptoms may have a discharge from the penis and a burning sensation when urinating. If symptoms of early infection do occur, they usually appear within 1 to 3 weeks of sexual contact with an infected person. Untreated infections may spread to other reproductive organs in both males and females, often without symptoms until permanent damage has occurred. A pregnant female can spread chlamydia to her baby during delivery, causing eye infection and sometimes pneumonia.

Diagnosis of chlamydia is made by testing a specimen collected from the infected site for bacteria. A more recent test involves checking a urine sample for bacteria. If chlamydia is diagnosed, antibiotics can easily cure the infection.

About 40 percent of females with untreated chlamydia will develop **pelvic inflammatory disease (PID)**, *a painful infection of the uterus, fallopian tubes, and/or ovaries*. Permanent damage to these structures can result, along with severe pelvic pain, infertility, and increased likelihood of ectopic pregnancy. An active chlamydia infection also makes it three to five times more likely that a female will become infected with HIV if she is exposed to it.

Gonorrhea

Gonorrhea is *an STD caused by bacteria that live in warm, moist areas of the body*. With 650,000 reported new cases each year in the United States, gonorrhea is an extremely common infectious disease. The bacterium *Neisseria gonorrhoeae* causes gonorrhea. This organism can thrive in mucous membranes of the cervix, uterus, and fallopian tubes in females; in the urethra in females and males; and also in the mouth, throat, and anus in females and males.

Teens and young adults have the highest incidence of gonorrhea. Among females, 15- to 19-year-olds have the highest reported rate; among males, the highest rate is among 20- to 24-year-olds.

Most males do have some symptoms of the disease when they are infected. These usually appear 2 to 5 days after infection, but it can take up to 30 days. Symptoms of genital infection include a burning sensation when urinating, a yellowish-white discharge from the penis, and sometimes painful or swollen testicles.

In females, the disease may go unnoticed because females often show no symptoms. Early symptoms in females are often so mild they are mistaken for another type of infection. Symptomatic females have a burning sensation when urinating and a yellow vaginal discharge that is sometimes tinged with blood. In a rectal infection, symptoms in both males and females may include anal discharge, itching, soreness, and bleeding, as well as painful bowel movements. Throat infection causes few symptoms.

Untreated gonorrhea in females can lead to pelvic inflammatory disease. In males, gonorrhea can cause epididymitis, an inflammation of the testicles that can cause sterility. Gonorrhea can also affect the prostate and cause scarring inside the urethra. In both sexes, gonorrhea can spread to the blood or joints, at which point the disease becomes life threatening.

Gonorrhea is treated with antibiotics. Chlamydia infection is often present in people with gonorrhea, so antibiotics to treat both conditions are usually given at the same time. People with gonorrhea are more likely to contract HIV if exposed; those with HIV infection and gonorrhea are also more likely to spread HIV.

Genital Herpes

Genital herpes is *an STD caused by the herpes simplex virus type 2 (HSV-2)*. According to the CDC, an estimated 45 million people in the United States currently have the disease. There are about 1 million new cases each year. One in four females and one in five males have the disease. The number of teens and young adults with HSV-2 is increasing dramatically.

A person infected with HSV-2 frequently has no symptoms. If symptoms do occur, it is usually within two weeks of exposure to the virus and consists of an outbreak of blisters on or around the genitals or rectum. Some people may also have a fever and swollen glands. After the blisters break, painful lesions remain that take two to four weeks to heal. Within a few weeks or months, another outbreak may occur, but it is usually less severe than the first. Typically a person has four or five such episodes in the first year but has fewer as the years go by.

What are a sexually active person's chances of contracting an STD?
Sexually active individuals are at high risk of contracting an STD. Three million teens contract an STD each year. One out of every four Americans will contract an STD at some point in his or her lifetime. About 75 percent of sexually active people have been infected with HPV. More than 20 percent have genital herpes. In one single act of unprotected sex with an infected person, a female teen has a 30 percent chance of getting genital herpes and a 50 percent chance of getting gonorrhea.

EMPHASIZE. Most states require routine administration of antibiotic eye drops to newborn babies to prevent blindness caused by gonorrhea.

The virus is spread from open sores during sexual contact, but it also can be released when lesions are not present. One reason so many people have HSV-2 is that once a person has been infected, he or she will always have the disease and can spread it to other people. Certain antiviral medications can reduce the duration and severity of episodes, but the virus itself remains forever in the person's system. Consistent and correct use of condoms can help protect against infections. However, condoms may not completely cover the sores and the virus may still be spread.

HSV-2 can be fatal to newborns if contracted from the mother during delivery. Pregnant females who have an active genital herpes infection have a cesarean delivery to protect the baby.

Health Skills Activity

Communication: Helping a Friend Solve a Problem

Julia and Briann grew up next door to each other and have always been really good friends. Briann takes Julia aside one day after school.

"I'm scared, Jules. You've got to help me."

Julia winces as Briann explains what's wrong.

"I've got these blisters on my ... you know ... down there. They're turning into really painful sores."

Julia shakes her head. Then Briann adds, "And I don't even know how I got whatever this is—Andre and I have fooled around a little but we've never done all that much, and he swore to me he'd never done anything with anyone else!"

"Oh, Briann," Julia says.

"Don't judge me, Jules. Just tell me what I'm supposed to do now."

Julia wonders what she should say to Briann.

What Would You Do?
Write a dialogue showing how Julia can use good communication to advise Briann.

1. Use "I" statements to tell how you feel.
2. Keep your tone respectful.
3. Provide a clear, organized message that states the problem.
4. Listen to the other person's side without interrupting.

Herpes simplex virus type 1 (HSV-1) is also common in the United States but is not considered an STD. HSV-1 causes cold sores—blisters on the mouth and lips of infected people. The virus can be spread by saliva to another person when lesions are present. An HSV-1 infection can occur on the genitals following oral-genital contact with a person who has a cold sore; oral-genital contact with a person with HSV-2 can also cause HSV-2 infection on the mouth. Anyone who has an active episode of HSV-1 or HSV-2 should avoid touching the lesions; careful personal hygiene, including hand-washing, helps prevent the spread of the herpes virus to other people and other areas of one's own body.

Remember that abstinence is the only 100 percent effective method to avoid contracting STDs. You can protect yourself from the risks of STDs by practicing abstinence from sexual activity before marriage and by using refusal skills to avoid situations in which you may be at risk. Choosing friends who support your decision to remain abstinent will help you in your commitment.

CRITICAL THINKING. Ask students why they think cesarean delivery protects a baby from HSV-2.

 Lesson 1 *Review*

LESSON 1 REVIEW ANSWERS ARE FOUND ON PAGE TM42.

Reviewing Facts and Vocabulary

1. Define *sexually transmitted infections (STIs)*, and explain why they are difficult to track.

2. Describe the relationship between high-risk behaviors and the risk for contracting STDs.

3. What is human papillomavirus, and how common is it?

4. What is the most commonly reported bacterial STD in the United States, and why is it one of the most dangerous STDs?

5. Name some of the results of untreated gonorrhea.

Thinking Critically

6. **Synthesizing.** You and a friend have agreed to help each other remain abstinent. Your friend has just told you that she has accepted a date with a boy who has a reputation for being sexually active. What would you tell your friend about developing strategies to prevent the spread of STDs?

7. **Comparing.** How are the early symptoms for chlamydia and gonorrhea similar?

Applying Health Skills

Practicing Healthful Behaviors.
Communicate the importance of practicing abstinence from sexual activity. Make a pamphlet with guidelines teens can follow to avoid risky situations and behaviors that may compromise their decision to practice abstinence.

Other Sexually Transmitted Infections

VOCABULARY

hepatitis B (HBV)
syphilis
vaginitis
trichomoniasis
bacterial
 vaginosis (BV)
pubic lice
scabies

YOU'LL LEARN TO

- Develop and analyze strategies to prevent spreading sexually transmitted diseases.

- Explain the relationship between drug use and unsafe situations that can lead to transmission of STDs.

- Identify, describe, and assess community health services available for prevention and treatment of STDs.

- Analyze the importance and benefits of abstinence in the prevention of STDs.

QUICK START List two or more effects of STDs. Write two refusal skills you can use to avoid the consequences of contracting STDs.

Some of the other STDs you should know about include hepatitis B, syphilis, trichomoniasis, bacterial vaginosis, pubic lice, and scabies.

Hepatitis B

Hepatitis B (HBV) is *a viral STD that attacks the liver and can cause extreme illness and death.* HBV is transmitted when blood or other body fluids from an infected person enter the body of a person who is not immune to the disease. The virus is spread through sexual activity. Drug users who share needles can also get the virus from infected people, as can people who get tattoos or body piercing from facilities where instruments are not sterilized or inks are used more than once. An infected mother can also pass the virus to her baby during delivery.

Hepatitis B is transmitted through contact with the blood of someone who is infected, and can be spread through body-piercing needles.

In the United States today, three doses of hepatitis B vaccine are routinely administered to infants. Children and adolescents who were not immunized as infants receive the vaccine during later visits to their pediatrician.

Of the estimated 200,000 people in the United States who contract the disease each year, about 120,000 infections are due to sexual activity. About 417,000 people now have a chronic sexually acquired HBV infection; 5,000 to 6,000 people die each year from liver disease caused by chronic HBV infection.

About 30 percent of people with HBV have no symptoms. When symptoms occur, they include jaundice, fatigue, abdominal pain, nausea and vomiting, joint pain, and loss of appetite. People infected with HBV can be treated with drugs that are effective in about 40 percent of individuals. Approximately 15 to 25 percent of people with chronic HBV infections die of related liver disease.

A vaccine against HBV has been available since 1982; it is routinely given to children from birth to age 18. Health care and public safety workers, and anyone else exposed to blood or other body fluids, should also be vaccinated against HBV.

Hepatitis C

The hepatitis C virus, a blood-borne infection, is on the rise. According to the CDC, approximately 4 million Americans are infected. This disease can lead to chronic liver disease, liver cancer, and liver failure. Chronic hepatitis C is often asymptomatic, and the disease progresses slowly. Infected individuals may not realize they have the disease until damage shows up in routine physical examinations. Hepatitis C is transmitted through sexual contact and other direct contact with contaminated blood, such as contaminated needles used in injection drug use. There is no cure for hepatitis.

Syphilis

Syphilis is *an STD caused by the bacterium Treponema pallidum, and it progresses in stages.* Currently, the number of syphilis cases in the United States is at its lowest level since record keeping was initiated in 1941, but it remains a serious concern. Left untreated, syphilis causes severe, sometimes fatal damage to internal organs.

Syphilis is spread by direct contact with a chancre, a painless sore that appears early in the disease, or with the infectious rash that

The Consequences of STDs

Be aware of the problems STDs can cause:

▶ Some STDs are incurable and medical treatment can't eliminate them from the body.

▶ Some STDs can cause cancer. HPV is associated with cancer of the cervix, and the hepatitis B virus with cancer of the liver. Both of these STDs are incurable.

▶ Some STDs can cause complications that affect the ability to reproduce. PID, for example, damages a female's reproductive organs.

▶ Some STDs can be passed from an infected female to her child before, during, or after birth. STDs can damage the bones, nervous system, and brain of a fetus.

CRITICAL THINKING. Have students evaluate the following situation: A person with a small sore on his or her genitals puts some medicated cream on the sore and it goes away. The person says he or she does not need to see a doctor about it because it has gone away.

EMPHASIZE. Stress to students that although there are nonprescription treatments for some types of vaginitis, it is important to see a doctor to ensure a correct diagnosis.

appears later. Syphilis is transmitted primarily through sexual activity, including vaginal, oral, and anal sex. Pregnant females who have untreated syphilis can pass the disease to the fetus during pregnancy, which can cause stillbirth or death of the infant shortly after birth. Untreated, infected infants may have developmental delays, have seizures, or die from the disease.

Untreated syphilis progresses through three stages:

Primary Stage. Within 10 to 90 days of infection, a small, firm, round sore called a chancre appears at the spot where the bacterium entered the body. The sore is painless and lasts for 3 to 6 weeks, when it disappears, even without treatment.

Secondary Stage. An infectious rash of rough, red or reddish-brown spots appears on the palms of the hands and the soles of the feet. Flulike symptoms, hair loss, and weight loss can also be present. The rash disappears without treatment.

Late Syphilis. During a latent period usually lasting some years, external signs of the disease disappear. The organism remains in the body, however, damaging organs including the brain, nerves, eyes, heart, blood vessels, liver, bones, and joints. Symptoms of late syphilis include slow, progressive loss of muscle coordination, paralysis, blindness, and dementia. If damage to tissues is severe enough, death follows.

Syphilis is diagnosed by a blood test or by laboratory examination of material from the primary chancre or secondary-stage rash. The disease is easily cured with antibiotics, but once damage to internal organs has occurred, there is no way to repair the damage. People who are infected with syphilis are more likely to contract and transmit HIV through sexual contact.

Trichomoniasis and Bacterial Vaginosis

There are many types of **vaginitis**, *inflammation of the vagina caused by various organisms*. Only two, however, are sexually transmitted; both diseases are treated with the prescription drug metronidazole. **Trichomoniasis**, *an STD caused by the parasite Trichomonas vaginalis*, affects both females and males. Infected males experience symptoms only rarely—irritation inside the penis, mild discharge, or slight burning after urinating or ejaculating. Infected females often have symptoms that appear 5 to 28 days after exposure, including a foamy, yellow-green vaginal discharge that has a strong odor. Trichomoniasis in females can also cause genital irritation and itching and discomfort during intercourse and urination.

Bacterial vaginosis (BV), *an STD caused by an imbalance of bacteria normally found in the vagina*, affects only females. Little is known about the cause, but having sexual intercourse with a new partner and douching may be contributing factors. Symptoms, when present, include white or gray vaginal discharge with a strong odor as well as itching and burning around the vagina. BV increases the risk of gonorrhea and may lead to PID, endangering the uterus and fallopian tubes. Both trichomoniasis and BV can make HIV infection more likely.

Pubic Lice

Pubic lice, also known as "crabs," are *tiny parasitic insects that infest the genital area of humans*. Pubic lice are usually spread through sexual contact, and in rare circumstances, from infested bed linens, towels, and clothing since the lice can live a short time away from their host.

The main symptom of lice is intense itching. The lice usually live in pubic hair but can also live in the coarse hair of legs, armpits, mustaches, beards, eyebrows, and eyelashes. Lice that infest the hair on a person's head are not pubic lice.

Special medicated shampoos that kill pubic lice are available over the counter and with a doctor's prescription. These shampoos are harsh and should not be used on the eyebrows or eyelashes. For this, a special ointment that will not damage the eyes is available by prescription.

Scabies

Scabies is *an infestation of the skin with microscopic mites called Sarcoptes scabiei*. Scabies is spread through sharing of infested bedding and clothing and through prolonged skin-to-skin contact. Scabies is not transmitted by shaking someone's hand.

Symptoms appear 4 to 6 weeks after contact and include a pimplelike rash, particularly between the fingers and in skin folds on the body, but also on the penis, breast, and shoulder blades. The rash causes severe itching; sores can become infected from scratching. Fewer than ten mites are usually present on an infested person, so diagnosis of scabies can be difficult. Examining the burrows made by the mites provides the best means of diagnosis. All people who live in infected people's households, along with all sexual partners of infested people, should be treated at the same time as the infected person with special lotions that kill the mites.

CRITICAL THINKING. Remind students that pubic lice and scabies can be transferred from person to person through clothing and bed linens. Ask students what actions someone being treated for pubic lice or scabies might take to ensure the cleanliness of their clothing and linens.

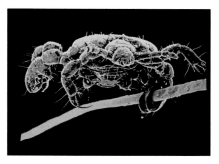

(A) Special medicated shampoos help eliminate pubic lice.

Did You Know ?

Using a latex condom can provide some protection from the spread of certain STDs, including bacterial vaginosis, gonorrhea, chlamydia, syphilis, and HIV. However, it does not protect against all STDs. For example, HSV-2, HPV, pubic lice, and scabies are easily transmitted through contact with an infected area not covered by the condom.

Facts About STDs:

- Because the body does not build up immunity to STDs, reinfection can occur.
- Although symptoms of some STDs may go away without treatment, the disease remains in the body.
- It is possible to have an STD and not know it.
- Unbroken skin is a barrier against pathogens, so there is almost no chance of getting an STD from a toilet seat, doorknob, handrail, or public telephone.
- A person can have more than one STD at the same time.

Treating STDs

STDs can be prevented, and it is every individual's responsibility to practice behaviors that prevent the spread of STDs. Obtaining treatment for STDs is also an important responsibility. STDs will not go away if a person waits long enough; he or she must seek treatment from a doctor or a public health clinic. For treatment to be successful, a person must:

► Follow the doctor's orders for treatment and take all the medication prescribed. Never stop taking the medication just because the symptoms have gone away.

► Notify everyone with whom he or she has had any sexual contact.

► Remember that abstinence is the only effective method of preventing reinfection or transmission of STDs now and in the future.

If a person doesn't know where to go for help, he or she should consult an STD hot line. Calls are anonymous, and the people who handle the calls are trained to give good advice.

DISCUSSING. Ask students how one might overcome the embarrassment of telling a partner that he or she has an STD.

Lesson 2 *Review*

LESSON 2 REVIEW ANSWERS ARE FOUND ON PAGE TM43.

Reviewing Facts and Vocabulary

1. Explain the relationship between drug use and unsafe situations. What is hepatitis B and how is it transmitted?
2. How is syphilis spread?
3. Which two types of vaginitis are sexually transmitted?
4. What is the main symptom of pubic lice?
5. What is scabies?

Thinking Critically

6. **Synthesizing.** If the number of cases of syphilis in the United States is at its lowest level since 1941, why does it remain a serious concern? Analyze strategies to prevent the spread of this STD.

7. **Analyzing.** Analyze the importance and benefits of abstinence. How can teens ensure that they do not contract an STD?

Applying Health Skills

Communication Skills. Identify, describe, and assess community health services available for the prevention and treatment of STDs. Suppose that a friend came to you and told you that he had a painless sore on the genitals that disappeared within two weeks. What would you advise him to do first? After he sees a doctor, what advice would you give him?

Chapter 7 *Review*

CHAPTER 7 REVIEW ANSWERS ARE FOUND ON PAGE TM44.

➤ REVIEWING FACTS AND VOCABULARY

1. Tell which of the following statements is true:
   a. A person can always tell if a sexual partner has an STD.
   b. A person cannot get an STD if he or she has only one sexual partner.
   c. A person could have an STD and not know it.

2. Describe the relationship between high-risk behaviors and the risk of contracting an STD. What is the most effective way to avoid getting an STD?

3. Can only males, only females, or both get chlamydia?

4. What is pelvic inflammatory disease? What can result from this STD?

5. How is HPV diagnosed and treated?

6. Why do so many people have HSV-2?

7. Describe the secondary stage of syphilis.

8. How would a doctor determine whether a person has syphilis?

9. Explain how pubic lice are treated.

10. Identify and describe community health services available for prevention and treatment of STDs. Where should a person go for treatment of an STD?

➤ THINKING CRITICALLY

11. **Synthesizing.** In terms of prevention, how are STDs different from most other communicable diseases, such as the common cold?

12. **Analyzing.** Do you think doctors should be required to inform the parents of a patient under the age of 18 who has an STD? Why or why not?

13. **Evaluating.** What would you advise if your friend told you that he or she had pubic lice?

14. **Synthesizing.** What might be the consequences if a person infected with an STD never told his or her sexual partners that he or she had an STD?

15. **Analyzing.** Explain why prevention and treatment of STDs is the responsibility of every individual.

➤ APPLYING HEALTH SKILLS

16. **Advocacy.** Analyze the importance and benefits of abstinence in the prevention of STDs. Write a 30-second radio announcement promoting prevention of STDs in your community.

17. **Analyzing Influences.** Write an essay in which you explain why you think STDs are such a serious problem in the adolescent age group.

BEYOND *the* Classroom

Parent Involvement

Discussing. Discuss with your parents or guardians the issues of STDs, medical information, and privacy for minors under the age of 18. Discuss whether adolescents, adults, or anyone should be required to inform anyone else of their STD.

School and Community

Report to the class. Do research at the library or on the Internet to find further information on a particular STD. Write a report to share with the class. Include symptoms, diagnosis, treatment, and dangers that can occur when the STD is not treated. Include a visual aid when presenting the report to the class.

HIV and AIDS

Quick**Write**

Using Visuals. Researchers are working to improve diagnostic methods to identify HIV so that early treatment is possible. List ways you know that HIV can be transmitted.

What Is HIV/AIDS?

VOCABULARY

acquired immune deficiency
  syndrome (AIDS)
human immunodeficiency
  virus (HIV)
lymphocytes
antibodies
AIDS-opportunistic
  illnesses (AIDS-OIs)

YOU'LL LEARN TO

- Identify the stages and symptoms of HIV infection and AIDS.

- Explain the relationship between risky behaviors, unsafe situations, and the transmission of HIV.

- Explain why abstinence from alcohol, drugs, and sexual activity is the only method that is 100 percent effective in preventing HIV infection.

QUICK START   Imagine that a friend needs some advice. Your friend has been abstinent for a year, but had been sexually active for a brief period before that. Your friend is considering being tested for HIV. Write out your advice to him or her on a piece of paper.

Acquired immune deficiency syndrome (AIDS) is *a fatal disorder that interferes with the body's natural ability to fight infection.* AIDS has exploded into a global health crisis, with no fully effective treatment or known cure. AIDS is the final stage of infection with the **human immunodeficiency virus (HIV)**, *a virus that attacks the immune system.* Since 1995, the number of new cases of AIDS has been decreasing steadily in the United States. Unfortunately, worldwide statistics are not as promising.

CRITICAL THINKING. Ask students to consider why the number of new cases of HIV/AIDS has not decreased as much in other countries as it has in the United States.

History and Origin of HIV

The first reported cases of AIDS were diagnosed in the United States in 1981. The earliest identified case of HIV infection dates back to 1959; however, some scientists believe the virus may have been infecting humans since 1930 or earlier. Males and females of all races, ages, and sexual orientations can and have become infected with HIV.

How Does HIV Affect the Body?

To understand how HIV attacks the body's immune system, it is necessary to review the functions of lymphocytes. **Lymphocytes** are *specialized white blood cells made in bone marrow that provide the body with immunity*. They move throughout the lymphatic system to help the body fight pathogens, or disease-causing organisms. Two types of lymphocytes work to protect against diseases: B cells, which mature in bone marrow, and T cells, which mature in the thymus gland. T-helper cells, a type of T cell, stimulate B cells to produce **antibodies**, which are *proteins that help destroy pathogens that enter the body*.

HIV enters certain cells, including T-helper cells, and reproduces itself. As more cells are infected, more are destroyed, and the immune system becomes weakened and is eventually destroyed. The body succumbs to **AIDS-opportunistic illnesses (AIDS-OIs)**, *infections the body could fight off if the immune system were healthy*.

HIV infection usually goes through identifiable stages. The process can take up to ten years before HIV infection progresses to AIDS. In a small number of people infected ten or more years ago, there have been no symptoms of AIDS. Researchers are investigating whether this is due to a difference in their immune systems, infection with a less aggressive strain of HIV, or a gene that protects them from HIV effects.

▶ **Asymptomatic Stage.** For a span of years, the virus is largely confined to the lymph nodes, where it invades and takes over or destroys T-helper cells. There are no outward signs of infection—the person can look and feel healthy.

▶ **Middle Stage.** Symptoms appear as the T-helper cell count falls to about 400 per milliliter of blood (an uninfected person has approximately 1,200). The infected person experiences flulike symptoms such as headache, fever, body aches, swollen glands, diminished appetite, unexplained weight loss, and skin rashes. Toward the end of this stage, AIDS-OIs begin to increase.

▶ **AIDS Stage.** The T-helper cell count drops to less than 200 or one or more of the AIDS-OIs are present. It is these AIDS-OIs that can cause the suffering and death typical of AIDS.

How HIV Is Transmitted

For a person to contract HIV, the virus must enter the individual's blood. HIV is carried in body fluids such as blood, semen, vaginal secretions, and breast milk. A person may come in contact with such infected body fluids and contract the virus if

All health care workers now wear protective gear to eliminate the risk of contracting or spreading HIV. *Which body fluids are known to carry HIV?*

there are breaks in the skin such as cuts, sores, or tiny breaks in the capillaries of mucous membranes. Use of contaminated needles and injected drug use also puts a person at risk.

Behaviors Known to Transmit HIV

Certain activities are far more likely than others to transmit HIV. Nearly 100 percent of new HIV infections in the United States are contracted in one of two ways: sexual activity with an infected partner accounts for about 75 percent, and injection drug use accounts for about 25 percent.

▶ **Sexual Contact.** Unprotected sexual activity with an infected partner is the main way that HIV is spread. HIV is present in an infected person's vaginal secretions or semen and is also present in pre-ejaculatory fluid that is primarily secreted from the Cowper's glands. During sexual contact, the virus usually enters the body through tiny tears in fragile tissue or breaks in capillaries of mucous membranes. Such tears and breaks are common during genital-genital, oral-genital, and anal-genital contact. The larger the number of sex partners a person has, the greater the risk of coming in contact with HIV. People with other STDs that result in sores, bleeding, or discharge are more likely to contract and transmit HIV.

▶ **Contaminated Needles.** When a drug user injects drugs with a needle, blood remains on and within the needle after use. If the person is infected with HIV, the virus can be spread to someone else who uses that needle. Sharing any kind of needles, whether to inject drugs, make tattoos, or do body piercing puts a person at risk for coming in contact with HIV. Recent studies have found that, in addition to needle-sharing, people who abuse injection drugs are more likely to engage in high-risk behaviors such as having unprotected sexual intercouse of any kind.

Situations Known to Transmit HIV

HIV can be transmitted whenever blood from an infected person is handled if precautions are not followed.

▶ **Blood Transfusion.** People who donate blood are not at risk for contracting HIV since blood donation centers discard needles after each use. Since March 1985, all donated blood in the United States has been tested for HIV. This has almost completely eliminated the risk of contracting HIV from a blood transfusion.

▶ **Before, During, and After Birth.** A pregnant female infected with HIV can pass the virus to her unborn baby through the placenta. During birth, HIV can enter the baby's

EMPHASIZE. Stress again that the most common ways HIV is spread—sexual intercourse and sharing IV needles—are choice- and behavior-related. Each individual has the opportunity to make healthful decisions to prevent the spread of HIV.

 Blood that is donated in the United States is tested for HIV.

DISCUSSING. Ask students to discuss how HIV/AIDS education might help in the fight against HIV/AIDS.

body through tiny cuts in the skin. After birth, a breastfed baby can contract HIV from the mother's milk. Approximately one-quarter to one-third of untreated infected females who get pregnant pass the virus on to their babies. Special drugs given to the mother during pregnancy can greatly reduce the baby's risk of contracting HIV. Drug treatment and delivery by cesarean section lowers the risk to about 1 percent.

How HIV Is Not Transmitted

The thought of contracting HIV is frightening, but remember that it can only be transmitted through contact with certain body fluids, including blood, semen, vaginal secretions, and breast milk. HIV cannot be spread through casual contact such as shaking hands, touching, or hugging. Even within families of an infected individual, HIV is not spread by sharing towels, combs, eating utensils, or bathroom facilities. HIV is not airborne, so it cannot be spread by coughing or sneezing, nor is it transmitted by the bites of insects such as mosquitoes.

Teens at Risk

Because sexually active teens tend to engage in high-risk behaviors, they are at serious risk for HIV/AIDS. The U.S. government's Centers for Disease Control and Prevention (CDC) gathers statistics on disease throughout the nation and the world. The following statistics clarify the threat posed by HIV for U.S. teens who engage in high-risk behaviors.

▶ Each year, about 40,000 new cases of HIV infection occur in the United States; half of these cases occur in people under the age of 25.

▶ The cases of AIDS among people between the ages of 13 and 19 reported to the CDC as of June, 2001 totaled 4,219.

▶ HIV is the seventh leading cause of death among U.S. children ages 5 to 14; it ranks sixth for young people ages 15 to 24.

HIV Prevention

In recent years, there has been progress in treating AIDS and AIDS-opportunistic illnesses. Many people are living symptom free for longer periods of time; a mother with HIV has a better chance of not transmitting it to her baby; people have become educated about the virus and are taking more precautions to protect themselves from coming in contact with it. Despite this progress, HIV/AIDS remains an incurable condition. Because HIV/AIDS is preventable, however, avoiding risk behaviors is the best defense against infection.

Staying Informed

There are many sources of dependable information about HIV infection and AIDS. Reputable newspapers, magazines, and health segments on television and radio programs offer the latest scientific findings. Reliable sites on the Internet, such as government agencies and medical associations, also offer accurate updates. Many people, such as school counselors, religious leaders, and doctors, are knowledgeable in this area, or can provide guidance in locating other reliable information sources.

During your teen years, you may feel pressure to experiment with new behaviors, such as engaging in sexual activity and/or using alcohol or other drugs. Remember that your decisions will have an impact on the rest of your life, and that the only responsible decision is to choose abstinence from sexual activity before marriage and avoid all drug use, especially injection drug use. Here are some strategies to help you avoid pressure to engage in sexual activity or use drugs.

▶ Avoid situations in which pressure is almost certain. If you are at a party where the situation is out of control, leave.

▶ Avoid being alone with a date in a private place. Avoid forming a dating relationship with someone whom you know to be sexually active.

▶ Avoid the use of alcohol and other drugs. Avoid known drug users and those who approve of drug use.

▶ When you use refusal strategies, be firm and unwavering. Use body language to reinforce your message.

EMPHASIZE. Stress to students that, as research on HIV/AIDS continues, information about HIV/AIDS is constantly changing. Reliable Internet sites such as the CDC can be useful in ensuring that your information is up to date and accurate.

 Lesson 1 *Review*

LESSON 1 REVIEW ANSWERS ARE FOUND ON PAGE TM46.

Reviewing Facts and Vocabulary

1. What is AIDS and how is it related to HIV?

2. Describe the asymptomatic stage of AIDS.

3. Explain the relationship between risk behaviors, unsafe situations, and HIV/AIDS. Explain the ways in which HIV is known to be transmitted.

4. Are all teens at serious risk for HIV/AIDS?

Thinking Critically

5. **Analyzing.** Do you think an individual infected with HIV is responsible for informing others of the infection? Why or why not?

6. **Synthesizing.** Why is AIDS a serious threat to public health?

Applying Health Skills

Advocacy. Explain why abstinence from alcohol, drugs, and sexual activity is the only method that is 100 percent effective in preventing HIV/AIDS. Design a poster that tells teens how to avoid HIV infection and how to avoid high-risk situations that challenge their decision to abstain from sexual activity and all drug use, especially injection drug use.

HIV/AIDS Testing and Treatment

VOCABULARY

EIA
Western blot test
pneumocystis carinii
 pneumonia (PCP)
Kaposi's sarcoma (KS)
cytomegalovirus (CMV)
candidiasis
community outreach
 programs
grief counselor

YOU'LL LEARN TO

- Describe the tests that are used to diagnose the presence of HIV antibodies.

- Identify the symptoms of HIV infection and AIDS.

- Explain how technology and the use of various drugs and combinations of drugs are used in the treatment of AIDS.

- Identify, describe, and assess support services available in the community for individuals with HIV/AIDS and their families.

QUICK START In the first column of a two-column table, identify three or more conditions, careers, or other circumstances that you believe make it especially important for people to be tested for HIV infection. Explain your reasoning in the second column.

CRITICAL THINKING. Ask students why they think testing for HIV is recommended for medical workers. Why might medical workers face an increased risk of contracting HIV?

Within a few years of the diagnosis of the first cases of AIDS in the United States, tests were developed to detect HIV infection. Currently, all donated blood must be tested for HIV. Anyone who donates body organs or tissue, as well as people joining the armed forces, must undergo testing. Testing is also recommended for medical workers.

Detecting HIV Antibodies

When HIV enters a person's body, the immune system produces antibodies to destroy the pathogen. Unfortunately, the antibodies produced in response to HIV are unable to completely eliminate the virus from the body. HIV tests can detect these antibodies, however, making them useful for diagnosis. It takes an average of 25 days for detectable antibodies to develop, but it may take 6 months or longer in some people.

EIA and Confirmatory Tests

E IA, or ELISA, is *a test used to detect the presence of antibodies for HIV in blood*. The EIA (enzyme immunoassay) was developed in 1985 and is the standard screening tool for HIV infection. EIA tests may require several weeks or months for the results to be received. A more costly test for HIV has recently been approved by the Food and Drug Administration (FDA) for use in the United States. Test results are usually available in 15 to 30 minutes. If test results are positive, an additional blood test is needed for confirmation.

If an EIA or rapid HIV test shows a reaction, the test is repeated. If the results are again reactive, a confirmatory test such as the Western blot or the IFA (immunofluorescent antibody) test is used. The **Western blot test** and the IFA are *specific tests used in identifying HIV antibodies*. Confirmatory test results generally take one to two weeks. If these test results are positive, a person is considered to be infected with HIV. An infected person who may be symptom free for many years can still infect others when engaging in any activities known to transmit HIV.

Even with a negative result from an EIA or a rapid HIV test, a person might still be infected with HIV because, in some people, it can take the immune system six months or more to develop HIV antibodies. If a person believes he or she was exposed to HIV and test results are negative, a second test should be performed about six months later. If that test is also negative, the person is probably not infected with HIV. During the time when there is doubt, however, activities that could transmit the virus must be avoided.

Symptoms of HIV Infection

M any people have no early symptoms when they are infected with HIV, but some develop flulike symptoms a month or two after they are infected. These symptoms include fever, headache, fatigue, and swollen lymph nodes. Within one to four weeks, these symptoms usually disappear.

Within a few months to 10 years or more, an infected person will develop other symptoms. These include persistent swollen glands, lack of energy, weight loss, frequent fevers and sweats, persistent or frequent yeast infections, skin rashes, pelvic inflammatory disease in females, and short-term memory loss.

Did You Know ?

Certain factors can lead to a false-reactive EIA test:

- **Laboratory error.** At the laboratory where the blood is analyzed, samples are sometimes incorrectly labeled, or a nonreactive sample is accidentally contaminated by a nearby reactive sample.
- **Blood abnormalities.** Diseases of the blood have been linked to false-reactive tests. False reactions have been reported in some people with hemophilia and some alcoholic patients with hepatitis.
- **Pregnancy.** Women in a second or later pregnancy may have false-reactive readings.
- **Other conditions.** People who have certain conditions such as Lyme disease, syphilis, or lupus may have false-reactive readings.
- **A cross-reactivity with other retroviruses.** Although every virus is different, some have similar genetic makeups. For example, human T cell lymphoma/leukemia viruses (HTLV) have structures similar to HIV and, therefore, produce similar antibodies. The presence of HTLV in a person's blood might cause a false-reactive EIA.

Diagnosis of AIDS

The current CDC definition of AIDS requires that a person be HIV positive *and* have *either* a T-helper cell count below 200 *or* the presence of at least one AIDS-opportunistic illness (AIDS-OI). Some of the most common AIDS-OIs are:

▶ **Pneumocystis carinii pneumonia (PCP)**, *a fungal infection that causes a form of pneumonia*. This is the most common cause of pneumonia in people with AIDS; symptoms include difficulty breathing, fever, a dry cough, weakness, and weight loss.

▶ **Kaposi's sarcoma (KS)**, *a kind of cancer that develops in connective tissues*. KS usually appears in the skin or in the

Real-Life Application

The Cost of HIV/AIDS

The cost of HIV/AIDS in terms of suffering and death is immeasurable. Fortunately, mortality rates in the United States continue to decline. The rate of spending on HIV/AIDS-related issues is not declining, however. Look at the chart below. Which does the government spend more on each year: health care, research, or prevention? Has spending increased significantly more for one area than for another?

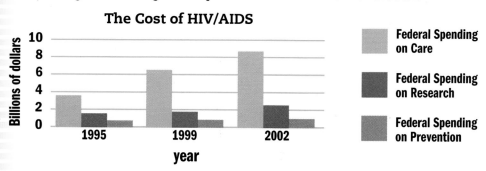

The Cost of HIV/AIDS

Legend:
- Federal Spending on Care
- Federal Spending on Research
- Federal Spending on Prevention

Source: The Kaiser Family Foundation. *Spending on the HIV/AIDS Epidemic, 2002*

ACTIVITY

There have been 3,694 cases of AIDS in people in the United States aged 13 through 19 reported to the CDC through June 2000. An estimated 3.75 million new cases of other STDs in teens are reported each year. Research government spending on one type of STD. Create a graph that compares your findings about the costs of STDs to the costs of HIV/AIDS.

linings of the mouth, nose, or anus. More serious cases involve the lungs, liver, gastrointestinal tract, and lymph nodes. KS causes flat, painless skin lesions that look like bruises.

▶ **Cytomegalovirus (CMV)**, *a virus found in 50 percent of the general population and 90 percent of people with HIV.* A weakened immune system allows this opportunistic infection to develop, and it can cause blindness, pneumonia, and gastrointestinal disease.

▶ **Candidiasis**, *an infection caused by a common type of yeast (fungus) found in almost everyone in the general population.* Candidiasis usually affects the mouth (thrush), throat (esophagitis), or vagina (vaginitis), and may persist or recur.

Research and Treatment

As yet, there is no cure for HIV infection or AIDS. Much progress has been made, however, in delaying the onset of AIDS and in treating AIDS-OIs. Individuals diagnosed with AIDS are living longer, and more comfortably, than ever before.

Drug Research

Antiretroviral drugs inhibit HIV from making copies of itself. The first such drugs developed to fight HIV were zidovudine (AZT), didanosine (ddI), and zalcitabine (ddC). These drugs, known collectively as Nucleoside Reverse Transcriptase Inhibitors (NRTIs), are still being used today.

Another class of drugs, called protease inhibitors (PIs), blocks the progress of HIV in later stages of reproduction within the body. Examples of these drugs are saquinavir, ritonavir, indinavir, and nelfinavir.

Yet a third class of drugs, known as Non-Nucleoside Reverse Transcriptase Inhibitors (NNRTIs), has also been added to the arsenal of weapons against AIDS. Examples of these drugs are nevirapine, delavirdine, and efavirenz. Like NRTIs, these drugs keep HIV from infecting new cells. Unfortunately, HIV quickly becomes resistant to NNRTIs when they are used alone.

Scientists now know that taking a combination of drugs is more effective than taking one drug alone. A "cocktail," or assortment, of drugs can minimize side effects and prevent HIV from becoming resistant to individual drugs. The current recommended treatment for HIV is a triple drug combination known as Highly Active Antiretroviral Therapy, or HAART. Combinations of NRTIS, PIs, and NNRTIs are used in this regimen.

What are the major obstacles to research and treatment of HIV/AIDS?

Despite the promise of cutting-edge research and treatment, a number of obstacles remain. Because HIV is constantly undergoing changes in its genetic structure, the virus has been able to build up resistance to medications used to fight it. Also, in connection with changes in genetic structure, several new strains of HIV have developed—further complicating the search for a vaccine. The treatments that have been developed are very expensive and some people cannot afford them. In addition, some individuals find it difficult to follow a rigid schedule for taking so many medicines—often with unpleasant side effects—each day.

EMPHASIZE. Stress to students that drugs to fight the symptoms of HIV/AIDS are treatments, not cures. Although they can slow its progress, they do not rid the body of HIV.

Drugs are said to be working if the level of virus in the blood decreases. By using a combination of drugs, some individuals are able to decrease their viral load to such an extent that it is undetectable in blood tests.

While combination-drug therapy has helped individuals infected with HIV/AIDS, there are many drawbacks to these drugs. AIDS drugs have very strong side effects, including nausea, vomiting, diarrhea, headaches, and intestinal distress. They are also very expensive, costing in the range of $12,000 to $20,000 a year in the United States. The regimen of drugs is also difficult to manage. Some combinations require as many as 20 pills a day that must be taken on a very rigid schedule. Despite progress in treatment, AIDS remains a difficult, and fatal, disease.

Vaccines

Medical researchers began trials on HIV vaccines in 1987. Since then, almost 60 vaccines have been studied worldwide. The original focus involved finding a protein that would cause the immune system to produce effective HIV antibodies and has expanded to include ways to stimulate production of T-killer cells to help fight off HIV infection. Researchers are studying live bacteria and viruses, as well as chemically synthesized HIV proteins, killed or weakened HIV, and manipulated genetic material. Scientists are hopeful that a safe, effective vaccine will be developed. Avoiding risky behaviors remains the only sure way to prevent HIV infection today.

Soup kitchens like this one provide hot meals to people who are homebound with HIV and AIDS.

Support from the Community

People with HIV/AIDS need medical care, but they also need other kinds of support to help them cope with their illness. Extra support often comes from **community outreach programs**, which are *organizations, staffed largely by volunteers, that provide a wide range of essential services to individuals suffering from HIV/AIDS, their families, and their loved ones.* Some of the services provided by community outreach programs include:

▶ **Practical assistance.** People with HIV/AIDS often need help finding housing as well as getting legal, social, mental health, and visiting-nurse services. Individuals with advanced AIDS-OIs may need help making meals, and some groups run soup kitchens that prepare and deliver food.

▶ **One-on-one support.** As HIV/AIDS progresses, individuals with AIDS may need help with daily activities such as shopping, cooking, and cleaning. Some groups establish a buddy system in which a volunteer helps an individual with daily chores and provides companionship and moral support.

▶ **Crisis counseling.** Crisis counselors help individuals cope with problems when they feel overwhelmed or out of control.

▶ **Grief counseling.** Most people with HIV/AIDS face a painful, lengthy illness that, for most, ends in death. A **grief counselor** is *a professional who is trained to help people deal with the issues of sickness, dying, and death.* He or she also can help individuals and their families and loved ones cope with and adjust to the realities of various AIDS-OIs.

▶ **Information dissemination.** Those infected with HIV need a way to obtain and interpret the latest accurate information on treatment and care of HIV/AIDS. Many community outreach programs sponsor an AIDS telephone hot line that people can call if they have questions. Some groups, particularly in larger cities, publish newsletters. The San Francisco-based Project Inform sponsors meetings throughout the United States to keep people up to date on the latest information. The CDC keeps a list of community support groups and maintains an AIDS hot line of its own.

DISCUSS. Have students discuss ways that a support system can benefit people with HIV/AIDS.

 Lesson 2 *Review*

LESSON 2 REVIEW ANSWERS ARE FOUND ON PAGE TM47.

Reviewing Facts and Vocabulary

1. What do HIV tests detect?

2. What precautions should a person take if his or her first test for HIV antibodies results are negative?

3. What does the current CDC definition of AIDS require?

4. Why is a combination of drugs used to treat HIV infection?

5. Identify and describe some of the services provided by community outreach programs for individuals with HIV/AIDS and their families.

Thinking Critically

6. **Comparing.** Explain how technology has impacted the health status of individuals with HIV/AIDS. How are the EIA and Western blot tests used?

7. **Analyzing.** Why do you think some people with HIV don't use the recommended combinations of drugs?

Applying Health Skills

Advocacy. Prepare a plan for a community outreach program that provides support to people with HIV/AIDS. Provide descriptions of the services that will be provided and information on how teens might get the word out about these services. Include a statement or slogan that would help convince others to join the program and give of their time and talents to help those in need.

Chapter 8 *Review*

CHAPTER 8 REVIEW ANSWERS ARE FOUND ON PAGE TM48.

➤ REVIEWING FACTS AND VOCABULARY

1. How does HIV destroy the immune system?

2. What are AIDS-opportunistic illnesses?

3. What is the main way HIV is spread?

4. List three ways HIV is not transmitted.

5. HIV/AIDS is not curable, but it is preventable. What are the best methods of prevention for teens?

6. List possible early symptoms of HIV. How long do they usually last?

7. How long can HIV stay in the body before a person shows symptoms of infection?

8. What is Kaposi's sarcoma? What parts of the body are affected in serious cases?

9. How do antiretroviral drugs work?

10. What are community outreach programs?

➤ THINKING CRITICALLY

11. **Synthesizing.** Why do you think many people are uninformed about HIV infection and AIDS?

12. **Evaluating.** Do you believe that people should be required to undergo a test for AIDS before being considered for employment or medical insurance? Why or why not?

13. **Analyzing.** Analyze the importance of abstinence from all sexual activity before marriage in reducing the risk of contracting HIV/AIDS. Explain why abstinence from alcohol, drugs, and sexual activity is the only method that is 100 percent effective in preventing HIV/AIDS.

14. **Applying.** Explain the relationship between risk behaviors and HIV/AIDS. A person has been engaging in behaviors that can lead to HIV infection. He has been tested for HIV and the result was negative. What should he do next?

➤ APPLYING HEALTH SKILLS

15. **Communication Skills.** With your parents or guardians, discuss whether you feel HIV testing should be required for health care providers.

16. **Refusal Skills.** What refusal strategies would you advise a teen to use if his or her peers were pressuring that teen to try using an injection drug just one time?

BEYOND the Classroom

Parent Involvement

Treating disease. At the present time, HIV/AIDS is incurable. Many diseases throughout history were also incurable until medical researchers found a way to combat them. With your parent or guardian, choose one of the following diseases and write a report on its history: polio; tuberculosis; pneumonia; bubonic plague; malaria.

School and Community

Local support. Find out what organizations in your community are helping people with AIDS. Make a list of these organizations and describe specific steps each is taking to help those suffering from AIDS.

A

Abortion Any termination of a pregnancy. (Ch. 6, 95)

Abstinence A deliberate decision to avoid harmful behaviors, including avoiding sexual activity before marriage and the use of alcohol, tobacco, and other drugs. (Ch.2, 22)

Acquaintance rape Rape by someone the victim knows. (Ch. 6, 97)

Acquired immune deficiency syndrome (AIDS) A fatal disorder that interferes with the body's natural ability to fight infection. AIDS is the final stage of infection caused by the human immunodeficiency virus (HIV). (Ch. 8, 117)

AIDS-opportunistic illnesses (AIDS-OIs) Infections the body could fight off if the immune system were healthy. (Ch. 8, 118)

Amniocentesis A procedure that reveals chromosomal abnormalities and certain metabolic disorders in the fetus. (Ch. 5, 75)

Amniotic sac A fluid-filled sac that surrounds the embryo. (Ch. 5, 64)

Antibodies Proteins that help destroy pathogens that enter the body. (Ch. 8, 118)

B

Bacterial vaginosis (BV) An STD caused by an imbalance of bacteria normally found in the vagina. (Ch. 7, 113)

Birth defect An abnormality in the structure or function of the body that is present at birth. Birth defects can be caused by abnormal genes or by environmental factors. (Ch. 5, 76)

Birthing centers Facilities that have homelike settings, are separate from a hospital, and offer medication-free births. (Ch. 5, 80)

Blastocyst A ball of cells with a cavity in the center. It is an early stage of prenatal development. (Ch. 5, 64)

Blended family A family consisting of two married adults who have children from a previous marriage living with them. (Ch. 4, 53)

C

Candidiasis An infection caused by a common type of yeast (fungus) found in almost everyone in the general population. (Ch. 8, 125)

Cervical cap A thimble-shaped, soft latex cup that fits snugly onto the cervix. It is a barrier method of contraception. (Ch. 6, 88)

Cervix The neck of the uterus. (Ch. 3, 37)

Cesarean birth A method of childbirth in which a surgical incision is made through the abdominal wall and uterus. The baby is lifted out through the incision. (Ch. 5, 78)

Chlamydia An STD that is caused by the bacterium *Chlamydia trachomatis*. (Ch. 7, 106)

Chorionic villus sampling (CVS) A test used to reveal genetic disorders and fetal age and gender. (Ch. 5, 75)

Cognitive Relating to the ability to reason and think out abstract solutions. (Ch. 1, 8)

Commitment A promise or a pledge. (Ch. 4, 49)

Communication The process through which you send messages to and receive messages from others. (Ch. 2, 19)

Community outreach programs Organizations, staffed largely by volunteers, that provide a wide range of essential services to HIV/AIDS patients, their families, and their loved ones. (Ch. 8, 126)

Condom A thin sheath of latex, plastic, or animal tissue that is placed on the erect penis to catch semen. It is a physical barrier to the passage of sperm into the vagina and toward the ovum. (Ch. 6, 85)

Conflict A disagreement, struggle, or fight. (Ch. 2, 20)

Contraception Prevention of pregnancy. (Ch. 6, 84)

Contraceptive implant A birth control procedure that involves the insertion of six small rods under the skin of a female's upper arm. The rods release small amounts of hormones that prevent the ovaries from releasing an ovum each month. (Ch. 6, 88)

Cytomegalovirus (CMV) A virus found in 50 percent of the general population and 90 percent of people with HIV. It is a common AIDS-opportunistic illness. (Ch. 8, 125)

D

Date rape Rape by someone the victim is dating. (Ch. 6, 97)

Developmental task An event that needs to occur during a particular age period for a person to continue his or her growth toward becoming a healthy, mature adult. (Ch. 1, 8)

Diaphragm A soft latex cup with a flexible rim that covers the entrance to the cervix. It is a barrier method of contraception. (Ch. 6, 87)

E

EIA, or ELISA A test used to detect the presence of antibodies for HIV in blood. *EIA* means "enzyme immunoassay." (Ch. 8, 123)

Embryo An implanted blastocyst from the time of implantation until about the eighth week of development. (Ch. 5, 64)

Empathy The ability to feel what others feel, to put yourself in someone else's place. (Ch. 1, 11)

Endocrine system A body system made up of ductless glands that secrete chemicals called hormones into the blood. (Ch. 1, 12)

Epididymis A highly coiled structure located on the back side of each testis. (Ch. 3, 30)

Episiotomy An incision made from the vagina toward the anus to enlarge the vaginal opening for delivery of a baby. (Ch. 5, 78)

F

Fallopian tubes Tubes on each side of the uterus that connect the uterus to the region of the ovaries. (Ch. 3, 37)

Fertility awareness methods (FAMs) Methods of contraception that involve determining the fertile days of the female's menstrual cycle and avoiding intercourse during those days. (Ch. 6, 86)

Fertilization The union of a single sperm and an ovum. (Ch. 5, 63)

Fetal alcohol syndrome (FAS) A condition of physical, mental, and behavioral abnormalities that can result when a pregnant female drinks alcohol. (Ch. 5, 73)

Fetus A developing baby from the end of the eighth week after fertilization until birth. (Ch. 5, 65)

G

Genes Units of heredity that determine which traits, or characteristics, offspring inherit from their parents. (Ch. 5, 67)

Genetic counseling A process in which the genetic histories of prospective parents are studied to determine the presence of certain hereditary diseases. (Ch. 5, 68)

Genital herpes An STD caused by the herpes simplex virus type 2 (HSV-2). (Ch. 7, 107)

Genital warts Soft, moist, pink or red swellings that appear on the genitals and are caused by the human papillomavirus. (Ch. 7, 105)

Goal Something you aim for that takes planning and work. (Ch. 1, 7)

Gonorrhea An STD caused by bacteria that live in warm, moist areas of the body, such as mucous membranes. (Ch. 7, 106)

Grief counselor A professional who is trained to help people deal with the issues of sickness, dying, and death. (Ch. 8, 127)

H

Hepatitis B (HBV) A viral STD that attacks the liver and can cause extreme illness and death. (Ch. 7, 110)

Heredity Genetic characteristics passed from parent to child. (Ch. 4, 55)

Heterosexual Someone who is sexually attracted to people of the opposite gender. (Ch. 6, 93)

Homosexual Someone who is sexually attracted to people of the same gender. (Ch. 6, 93)

Hormones Chemical substances produced in glands, which regulate the activities of different body cells and organs. (Ch. 1, 12; Ch. 3, 44)

Human immunodeficiency virus (HIV) A virus that attacks the immune system. (Ch. 8, 117)

Human papillomavirus (HPV) A virus that causes genital warts and warts on other parts of the body. (Ch. 7, 105)

I

IFA A specific test used in identifying HIV antibodies. *IFA* means "immunofluorescent antibody." (Ch. 8, 123)

Incest Sexual contact between family members who cannot marry by law. (Ch. 6, 96)

Intimacy A closeness between two people that develops over time. (Ch. 2, 23)

K

Kaposi's sarcoma (KS) A kind of cancer that develops in connective tissues. It is a common AIDS-opportunistic illness. (Ch. 8, 124)

L

Labor The process by which contractions gradually push the baby out of the uterus and into the vagina to be born. (Ch. 5, 77)

Lymphocytes Specialized white blood cells made in bone marrow that provide the body with immunity. (Ch. 8, 118)

M

Masturbation Touching one's own genitals for sexual pleasure. (Ch. 6, 92)

Menstruation The process of shedding the uterine lining. (Ch. 3, 38)

O

Oral contraceptives Hormone pills that, taken correctly, create changes in the female body that prevent pregnancy; also called birth control pills. (Ch. 6, 87)

Ovaries The two female sex glands, which produce mature ova and female hormones. (Ch. 3, 37)

Ovulation The process of releasing one mature ovum each month into a fallopian tube. (Ch. 3, 37)

P

Parenting Providing care, support, and love in a way that leads to a child's total development. (Ch. 4, 56)

Peer pressure The influence that people your own age may have on you. (Ch. 2, 18)

Pelvic inflammatory disease (PID) A painful infection of the uterus, fallopian tubes, and/or ovaries. (Ch. 7, 106)

Penis A tubelike organ that functions in sexual reproduction and elimination of body wastes. (Ch. 3, 30)

Pituitary gland The gland that controls much of the endocrine system. It is about the size of a pea and is located at the base of the brain. Besides growth hormones, the pituitary gland releases other hormones that affect the brain, glands, skin, bones, muscles, and reproductive organs. (Ch. 1, 13)

Placenta A structure that forms along the lining of the uterus as the embryo implants. Its blood-rich tissues transfer oxygen and nutrients to the embryo. (Ch. 5, 64)

Pneumocystis carinii pneumonia (PCP) A fungal infection that causes a form of pneumonia. (Ch. 8, 124)

Prenatal Occurring or existing before birth. (Ch. 5, 69)

Puberty The period of growth from physical childhood to physical adulthood when a person develops certain traits of his or her own gender. (Ch. 1, 12)

Pubic lice Tiny parasitic insects, also known as crabs, that infest the genital area of humans. (Ch. 7, 113)

R

Rape Any form of sexual intercourse that takes place against a person's will. (Ch. 6, 97)

Refusal skills Communication strategies that help you say no effectively when you are urged to take part in behaviors that are unsafe or unhealthful, or that go against your values. (Ch. 2, 25)

Rubella (German measles) A contagious disease caused by a virus that does not cause serious complications except in pregnancy. (Ch. 5, 73)

S

Scabies An infestation of the skin with microscopic mites called *Sarcoptes scabiei*. (Ch. 7, 113)

Scrotum A loose sac of skin that extends outside the body and contains the testes. (Ch. 3, 29)

Self-concept The mental image you have about yourself. It is your unique set of perceptions, ideas, and attitudes about yourself. (Ch. 1, 5)

Semen A mixture of sperm and glandular secretions. (Ch. 3, 30)

Sexual abuse Any sexual contact that is physically or emotionally forced on a person against his or her will. (Ch. 6, 96)

Sexuality Everything about you as a male or female. It includes the way you act, your personality, and your feelings about yourself because you are male or female. (Ch. 1, 4)

Sexually transmitted diseases (STDs), sexually transmitted infections (STIs) Infections that spread from person to person through sexual contact. (Ch. 7, 103)

Single-parent family A family that consists of only one parent and one or more children. (Ch. 4, 59)

Sperm The male reproductive cells. (Ch. 3, 29)

Spermicide A chemical that kills sperm. (Ch. 6, 85)

Stereotype An idea or image held about a group of people that represents a prejudiced attitude, oversimplified opinion, or uninformed judgment. (Ch. 6, 93)

Sterilization A surgical procedure that makes a male or female incapable of reproducing. (Ch. 6, 90)

Syphilis An STD caused by the bacterium *Treponema pallidum*; it progresses in stages. (Ch. 7, 111)

T

Testes The male sex glands, which produce sperm and manufacture testosterone. (Ch. 3, 29)

Testosterone The male sex hormone produced by the testes. (Ch. 3, 29)

Trichomoniasis An STD caused by the parasite *Trichomonas vaginalis*. It affects both females and males. (Ch. 7, 112)

Tubal ligation A sterilization procedure for females in which the fallopian tubes are cut and tied or clamped to prevent sperm from reaching the ova. (Ch. 6, 90)

U

Ultrasound A test that produces an image on a screen by reflecting sound waves off the body's inner structures. (Ch. 5, 75)

Umbilical cord A ropelike structure that connects the embryo and the mother's placenta. (Ch. 5, 65)

Uterus A hollow, muscular organ that receives, holds, and nourishes the fertilized ovum during pregnancy. (Ch. 3, 37)

V

Vagina An elastic, muscle-lined tube that extends from the uterus to outside the body and is also called the birth canal. (Ch. 3, 36)

Vaginitis An inflammation of the vagina caused by various organisms. (Ch. 7, 112)

Values The beliefs and standards of conduct that are important to a person. (Ch. 2, 17)

Vas deferens A long tube that connects each epididymis with the urethra. (Ch. 3, 31)

Vasectomy A sterilization procedure for males in which each vas deferens is cut and sealed. (Ch. 6, 90)

Vulva External female reproductive organs. They consist of the mons pubis, labia majora (outer lips), labia minora (inner lips), vaginal opening, and clitoris. (Ch. 3, 35)

W

Western blot test A specific test that is used in identifying HIV antibodies. (Ch. 8, 123)

Withdrawal The male's removal of the penis from the vagina before ejaculation. (Ch. 6, 84)

Z

Zygote A fertilized ovum. (Ch. 5, 63)

A

Abortion/aborto Cualquier interrupción de un embarazo.

Abstinence/abstinencia Una decisión consciente de evitar la conducta peligrosa, como las relaciones sexuales antes del matrimonio y el uso del alcohol, tabaco y otras drogas.

Acquaintance rape/violación por un conocido Una violación perpetrada por alguien a quien la víctima conoce.

Acquired immune deficiency syndrome (AIDS)/síndrome de inmunodeficiencia adquirida (SIDA) Una afección mortal que interfiere con la habilidad natural del cuerpo de combatir infecciones. El SIDA es la etapa final de la infección causada por el virus de la inmunodeficiencia humana (VIH).

AIDS-opportunistic illnesses (AIDS-OIs)/enfermedades oportunistas del SIDA (EO del SIDA) Infecciones que el cuerpo podría combatir si el sistema inmune estuviera sano.

Amniocentesis/amniocentesis Procedimiento que muestra anormalidades en los cromosomas de un feto y ciertos trastornos metabólicos.

Amniotic sac/amnios Saco lleno de líquido que rodea el embrión.

Antibodies/anticuerpos Proteínas que ayudan a destruir los patógenos que entran en el cuerpo.

B

Bacterial vaginosis (BV)/vaginosis bacteriana Enfermedad de transmisión sexual causada por el desequilibrio de bacterias que normalmente están en la vagina.

Birth defect/defecto de nacimiento Anormalidad en la estructura o función del cuerpo que está presente al nacimiento. Puede ser el resultado de genes anormales o de factores ambientales.

Birthing centers/centros de parto natural Instalaciones que tienen un ambiente hogareño, están separados de los hospitales y ofrecen partos sin medicación.

Blastocyst/blastocisto Un balón de células con una cavidad en el centro. Es una de las etapas primeras del desarrollo prenatal.

Blended family/familia incorporada Una familia en que se casan dos adultos que tienen hijos de un matrimonio anterior viviendo con ellos.

C

Candidiasis/candidiasis Infección por un hongo que está presente en casi toda la gente.

Cervical cap/tapón cervical Una tapa de látex blanda en forma de dedal que se calza por encima de la apertura del útero o cérvix. Es un método anticonceptivo que forma una barrera.

Cervix/cérvix El cuello del útero.

Cesarean birth/parto por cesárea Un método de parto en el que se hace una incisión quirúrgica a través de la pared abdominal y el útero. El bebé se saca a través de la incisión.

Chlamydia/clamidia Una enfermedad de transmisión sexual causada por la bacteria *Chlamydia trachomatis*.

Chorionic villus sampling (CVS)/biopsia de vellosidades coriónicas Prueba utilizada para mostrar trastornos genéticos y la edad y el género del feto.

Cognitive/cognitivo Referente a la capacidad para pensar y llegar a soluciones abstractas.

Commitment/compromiso Un acuerdo o promesa.

Communication/comunicación Proceso por el cual envías mensajes y recibes mensajes de otros.

Community outreach programs/programas para ayudar a la comunidad Organizaciones dirigidas mayormente por voluntarios quienes proveen servicios esenciales para las personas con VIH/SIDA, sus familias y otros seres queridos.

Condom/preservativo o condón Una lámina fina de plástico, látex o tejido animal que se coloca en el pene erecto para recoger semen. Actúa como una barrera física, impidiendo que el semen entre en la vagina o pase hacia el óvulo.

Conflict/conflicto Desacuerdo, lucha o pelea.

Contraception/anticoncepción La prevención de embarazos.

Contraceptive implant/implante anticonceptivo Un procedimiento de control de natalidad en el que se insertan seis bastoncillos en la parte interna superior del brazo de una mujer. Los bastoncillos liberan pequeñas dosis de hormonas, impidiendo la emisión de un óvulo desde el ovario cada mes.

Cytomegalovirus (CMV)/citomegalovirus Virus que se encuentra en 50 por ciento del gran público y en 90 por ciento de la gente con VIH. Es una enfermedad oportunista del SIDA común.

D

Date rape/violación durante una cita Violación por alguien con quien la víctima sale.

Developmental task/tarea del desarrollo Un suceso que tiene que ocurrir a una edad determinada para que la persona pueda continuar su desarrollo hasta la madurez saludable.

Diaphragm/diafragma Un disco de látex blando con borde flexible que cubre la apertura del útero. Es un método anticonceptivo que forma una barrera.

E

EIA, or ELISA/EIA o ELISA Prueba para detectar la presencia de anticuerpos contra el VIH en la sangre. EIA, que son siglas en inglés, significa ensayo inmunológico enzimático.

Embryo/embrión Un blastocisto implantado, desde el momento de implantación hasta aproximadamente la octava semana de desarrollo.

Empathy/empatía La capacidad de sentir lo que otros sienten, de ponerse en el lugar de otro.

Endocrine system/sistema endocrino Un sistema del cuerpo compuesto de glándulas sin conductos que secretan sustancias químicas llamadas hormonas en la sangre.

Epididymis/epidídimo Una estructura en forma de madeja u ovillo ubicada detrás de cada testículo.

Episiotomy/episiotomía Una incisión hecha desde la vagina hacia el ano para agrandar el orificio vaginal durante el parto de un bebé.

────────── **F** ──────────

Fallopian tubes/trompas de Falopio Los tubos a ambos lados del útero que conectan el útero a la región de los ovarios.

Fertility awareness methods (FAMs)/Métodos anticonceptivos de abstinencia en días fértiles Métodos anticonceptivos que implican la determinación de los días fértiles en el ciclo menstrual de la mujer para no tener relaciones sexuales durante esos días.

Fertilization/fertilización La unión de una esperma con un óvulo.

Fetal alcohol syndrome (FAS)/síndrome de alcoholismo fetal Anormalidades físicas, mentales y de comportamiento que pueden ocurrir cuando una mujer embarazada toma alcohol.

Fetus/feto Un bebé en desarrollo, desde el fin de la octava semana después de fertilización hasta el nacimiento.

────────── **G** ──────────

Genes/genes Unidades de herencia que determinan qué rasgos o características los hijos heredan de los padres.

Genetic counseling/asesoría genética Proceso en el que se estudian las historias genéticas de los que quieren ser padres para determinar la presencia de ciertas enfermedades hereditarias.

Genital herpes/herpes genital Enfermedad de transmisión sexual causada por el virus del herpes simplex.

Genital warts/verrugas genitales Hinchazones blandas, rosadas o rojas e húmedas que aparecen en los órganos genitales. Son el resultado del papovavirus humano.

Goal/meta Algo que quieres alcanzar que requiere planificación y trabajo.

Gonorrhea/gonorrea Una enfermedad de transmisión sexual causada por bacterias que viven en las zonas cálidas y húmedas del cuerpo, por ejemplo las membranas mucosas.

Grief counselor/consejero de la tristeza Profesional que ayuda a la gente con los asuntos de la enfermedad y la muerte.

────────── **H** ──────────

Hepatitis B (HBV)/hepatitis B Enfermedad viral de transmisión sexual que ataca el hígado y puede causar otras enfermedades graves o la muerte.

Heredity/herencia Características genéticas transmitidas de padres a hijos.

Heterosexual/heterosexual Alguien que siente atracción sexual por personas del sexo opuesto.

Homosexual/homosexual Alguien que siente atracción sexual por personas del mismo sexo.

Hormones/hormonas Sustancias químicas que se producen en las glándulas y regulan la actividad de distintas células y órganos del cuerpo.

Human immunodeficiency virus (HIV)/virus de la inmunodeficiencia humana (VIH) Un virus que ataca el sistema inmune.

Human papillomavirus (HPV)/papovavirus humano (HPV) Virus que causa verrugas genitales y verrugas en otras partes del cuerpo.

────────── **I** ──────────

IFA/IFA Examen específico que se usa para identificar los anticuerpos del VIH. IFA, por sus siglas en inglés, significa anticuerpo imunofluorescente.

Incest/incesto Contacto sexual entre miembros de una familia que no pueden casarse por ley.

Intimacy/intimidad Un sentimiento de cercanía entre dos personas que se desarrolla a lo largo del tiempo.

────────── **K** ──────────

Kaposi's sarcoma (KS)/sarcoma de Kaposi Tipo de cáncer que se desarrolla en el tejido conectivo. Es una enfermedad oportunista del SIDA que es muy común.

────────── **L** ──────────

Labor/trabajo de parto El proceso por el cual contracciones gradualmente empujan el bebé fuera del útero hacia la vagina para nacer.

Lymphocytes/linfocitos Glóbulos blancos especializados que se producen en la médula ósea y proporcionan inmunidades al cuerpo.

────────── **M** ──────────

Masturbation/masturbación Tocarse los propios órganos genitales para obtener placer sexual.

Menstruation/menstruación El proceso de desprendimiento del revestimiento del útero.

────────── **O** ──────────

Oral contraceptives/anticonceptivos orales Píldoras de hormonas que cuando se toman correctamente hacen cambios en el cuerpo de una mujer que impiden el embarazo. También se llaman píldoras anticonceptivas.

Ovaries/ovarios Las dos glándulas sexuales femeninas que producen óvulos maduros y las hormonas sexuales femeninas.

Ovulation/ovulación La liberación de un óvulo maduro cada mes en una trompa de Falopio.

────────── **P** ──────────

Parenting/crianza Proveer cuidado, apoyo y amor de tal manera que conduzca al desarrollo total de un niño.

Peer pressure/presión de los compañeros La influencia que tus contemporáneos pueden tener sobre ti.

Pelvic inflammatory disease (PID)/enfermedad inflamatoria pélvica Una infección dolorosa del útero, de las trompas de Falopio y/o de los ovarios.

Penis/pene Un órgano tubular que tiene una función en la reproducción sexual y la eliminación de la orina.

Pituitary gland/glándula pituitaria La glándula que controla gran parte del sistema endocrino. Tiene aproximadamente el tamaño de un chícharo y está ubicada en la base del cerebro. Además de secretar las hormonas de crecimiento, la glándula pituitaria secreta otras hormonas que afectan el cerebro, otras glándulas, la piel, los huesos, los músculos y los órganos reproductores.

Placenta/placenta Una estructura que se forma a lo largo del revestimiento del útero al implantarse el embrión. Tejido rico en sangre transfiere oxígeno y nutrimentos al embrión.

Pneumocystis carinii pneumonia (PCP)/Neumonía por pneumocystis carinii Una infección de hongos que causa un forma de neumonía.

Prenatal/prenatal Que ocurre o existe antes del nacimiento.

Puberty/pubertad El período de crecimiento entre la infancia y la edad adulta desde el punto de vista físico cuando una persona desarrolla ciertas características de su propio género.

Pubic lice/ladillas Pequeñitos insectos parasíticos que infestan el vello púbico de personas.

━━━━━━━━━ **R** ━━━━━━━━━

Rape/violación Cualquier tipo de relación sexual que ocurre contra la voluntad de la persona.

Refusal skills/técnicas para rehusarse Estrategias de comunicación que te ayudan a decir que no cuando alguien te anima a participar en conducta que no es sana, es peligrosa, o está en contra de tus valores.

Rubella (German measles)/rubéola Enfermedad contagiosa causada por un virus que no tiene gran trascendencia, menos durante el embarazo.

━━━━━━━━━ **S** ━━━━━━━━━

Scabies/sarna Afección de la piel causada por insectos aradores muy pequeños que se llaman *Sarcoptes scabiei.*

Scrotum/escroto Un saco suelto de piel externo al cuerpo que contiene los testículos.

Self-concept/autoconcepto La imagen mental que tienes de ti mismo. Es tu conjunto único de percepciones, ideas y actitudes sobre ti mismo.

Semen/semen La mezcla de esperma y fluidos de las glándulas.

Sexual abuse/maltrato sexual Cualquier contacto sexual forzado física o emocionalmente contra la voluntad de una persona.

Sexuality/sexualidad Todo lo que se refiere a ti como hombre o mujer. Incluye la forma en que actúas, tu personalidad y tus sentimientos respecto de ti mismo por ser hombre o mujer.

Sexually transmitted diseases (STDs), sexually transmitted infections (STIs)/enfermedades de transmisión sexual (ETS), infecciones de transmisión sexual (ITS), Infecciones que se transmiten de persona en persona a través del contacto sexual.

Single-parent family/familia monoparental Una familia compuesta por un sólo padre y uno o más niños.

Sperm/esperma Las células reproductoras masculinas.

Spermicide/espermicida Un producto químico que mata a las espermas.

Stereotype/estereotipo Una idea o imagen acerca de un grupo de personas que representa una actitud prejuiciosa, una opinión simplista o un juicio sin fundamento.

Sterilization/esterilización Un procedimiento quirúrgico que hace que un hombre o una mujer sea incapaz de reproducirse.

Syphilis/sífilis Enfermedad de transmisión sexual causada por la bacteria llamada *Treponema pallidum.* La enfermedad progresa en etapas.

━━━━━━━━━ **T** ━━━━━━━━━

Testes/testículos Las glándulas sexuales masculinas que producen esperma y testosterona.

Testosterone/testosterona La hormona sexual masculina producida por los testículos.

Trichomoniasis/tricomoniasis Enfermedad de transmisión sexual causada por el parásito llamado *Trichomonas vaginalis.* Afecta a mujeres y a hombres.

Tubal ligation/ligadura de trompas Procedimiento de esterilización para mujeres en que las trompas de Falopio se cortan y se atan o cierran para impedir que la esperma llegue a los óvulos.

━━━━━━━━━ **U** ━━━━━━━━━

Ultrasound/ecografía o ultrasonido Un examen que produce una imagen en una pantalla al reflejar las ondas de sonido que chocan contra las estructuras internas del cuerpo.

Umbilical cord/cordón umbilical Una estructura como una cuerda que conecta el embrión con la placenta de la madre.

Uterus/útero Un órgano hueco y muy musculoso que recibe, mantiene y nutre el óvulo fecundado durante el embarazo.

━━━━━━━━━ **V** ━━━━━━━━━

Vagina/vagina Una vía tubular, muy elástica y muscular que se extiende desde el útero hasta afuera del cuerpo. También se llama el canal de parto.

Vaginitis/vaginitis Una inflamación de la vagina causada por varios organismos.

Values/valores Creencias y normas de conducta que son importantes para una persona.

Vas deferens/conducto deferente Un tubo largo que conecta el epidídimo con la uretra.

Vasectomy/vasectomía Un procedimiento de esterilización para hombres en que los conductos deferentes se cortan y se cierran.

Vulva/vulva Los órganos externos del sistema reproductor femenino. Consisten en el monte de Venus, los labios mayores y los labios menores, el orificio vaginal y el clítoris.

━━━━━━━━━ **W** ━━━━━━━━━

Western blot/Western blot Prueba muy específica para identificar los anticuerpos contra el VIH.

Withdrawal/coito interrumpido La extracción del pene por el hombre de la vagina antes de la eyaculación.

━━━━━━━━━ **Z** ━━━━━━━━━

Zygote/cigoto Un óvulo fertilizado.